A
Lancashire
Christmas

Compiled by John Hudson

ALAN SUTTON

First published in the United Kingdom in 1990
Alan Sutton Publishing Limited · Phoenix Mill ·
Far Thrupp · Stroud · Gloucestershire

First published in the United States of America in 1991
Alan Sutton Publishing Inc · Wolfeboro Falls ·
NH 03896–0848

British Library Cataloguing in Publication Data
A Lancashire Christmas.
1. English literature. Special subjects. Christmas –
Anthologies
I. Hudson, John *1946–*
820.8033

ISBN 0–86299–744–5

Library of Congress Cataloging in Publication Data
applied for

Cover illustration: Silent Night, *by Tom Dodson, from a range
of signed limited edition prints, copyright Studio Arts Publishing,
50 North Road, Lancaster LA1 1LT*

Typeset in Garamond 12/13
Typesetting and origination by
Alan Sutton Publishing Limited.
Printed and bound in Great Britain by
WBC, Bridgend, Mid Glam.

from

A Ragged Schooling

ROBERT ROBERTS

Robert Roberts wanted to be a journalist when he left school in Salford at the age of fourteen around the end of the First World War, and even told them as much at the Juvenile Labour Exchange. All he got for his presumption was an interview at the backstreet general engineering works just round the corner, and it was there, sure enough, that he began his working life.

This recollection of the concert party put on by the first-year apprentices at Christmas follows a series of accounts of the abuse and ill-treatment of these callow young boys. In the context of the book as a whole the ending is surprisingly soft-centred; though the image of the social outcast standing up to jeers, singing like an angel and hushing the audience to rapt silence is one beloved of Hollywood, one would not necessarily have expected it to hold good in the Salford slums of seventy years ago.

As Christmas time approached Tilson let it be known that the journeymen on whose behalf we had brewed so much tea and gone on so many errands would soon show themselves most appreciative. 'A lump sum,' Tich explained, 'is bein' col-

lected, and they divide it among all the first-year lads.' But beforehand, he warned, we would all have to perform at a concert to be given in front of our elders at dinner time on the last day before the holidays. This news filled us with alarm. What were we in for now?

In a free hour a week before Christmas a group of young apprentices gathered in the smithy, looking apprehensive. Two muscular men in leather aprons eyed us benevolently.

'You can't force us,' I said at once.

The smith flexed his large biceps. 'Maybe not; but there's been a concert in this 'ere firm every Christmas since Adam were a policeman, and there'll be one this year, see!' We shuffled about and looked glum. 'All I say is – you do a bit of a turn and we'll show usselves most generous!' He looked across at his striker. 'How much was it last year, Jud?'

'Oh, pounds an' pounds apiece!' lied his assistant, producing a pencil and paper. 'Who's first, now?'

By threat and persuasion they finally managed to get the

Weavers dressed for the first Christmas of this century at the
Victoria Mill in Clayton

names of about ten boys who, though fearful of the prospect, promised to sing, play an instrument, recite or 'do a sort of step dance' before the assembled works company. Only one apprentice resisted, a tall, thin lad in ill-fitting spectacles, already a butt, whom they called Lamp post. The very idea seemed to terrify him. 'Oh, no, mister! I just couldn't! Please!'

'Can you sing?' asked the striker.

'A-a little, b-but not before all them men!'

'I see,' said the smith. 'We'll have to coach this one a bit!'

And on Christmas Eve we entertained, standing on the bed of a great planing machine in the fitting shop, with a hundred or more men and youths crushed about the machinery before us. One by one the smith introduced his artistes. Any boy with the slightest claim to talent the assembly heard out and applauded. With a friend from our old school I had teamed up to harmonise in a sour rendition of *Sweet and Low*. This scored a certain *succès d'estime*; but those performers who made little effort to please left under a rain of ribaldry, fruit skins and oily cotton waste. At five minutes to siren time only the palsied Lamp post remained. Jud helped him, like an invalid, on to the planing machine bed. Unkindly, the audience laughed; improvers felt for their missiles. 'Lo, Hear the Gentle Lark!' roared the smith. They laughed again. The boy began to sing, tremulous but true, gathering courage *en route*; no one jeered. By the time he had finished the first lines a whole machine shop lay in silence. Then his voice took on power and sweetness, and, as he trebled, belts and pulleys above slid softly into motion for the afternoon shift. His notes rang out now, high and pure, to mingle with that gentle lapping. He ended, red with relief, to thundering applause, a clash of spanners on steel, and the scream of the works' hooter. The smith stood among us, smiling. With a showman's instinct he had saved his best turn for the finale. 'There's ten shillings for every one of you,' he bawled, 'and an extra ten for Lamp post!'

When Santa Claus Forgot

DAVID SMITH

In the immediate post-war years Christmases in Bury, as in all the Lancashire cotton towns, were far removed from the way they are now. There were no Christmas trees in the town centre, no Rotary Club carol broadcasts, very few brightly-lit shop windows filled with toys, sweets and festive fare. More to the point, in my case, there was no store in town with a Father Christmas, and it became a local tradition, and a valid reason for absence from school, for young children to be taken on the 'Lecki' for an afternoon of Christmas shopping in Manchester, the highlight being a visit to Santa's grotto at Lewis's.

One particularly cold Christmas my sister and I were accompanied on the trip to town by our cousins from the then remote village of Summerseat. Leaving the magic and wonder of Victoria Station, where the steam engines seemed to be huffing and puffing about purely for our delight, we ambled through the sidestreets, our hearts pounding as we pointed, tugged and pleaded at every colourful barrow and shop along the way. We eventually reached Lewis's in a wet and weary state, laden with parcels, tempers beginning to fray. It cheered us up no end to see the look of simple faith

Father Christmas at the old Owen Owen store in Fishergate,
Preston, in 1969

SKETCHES AT WHAITE'S GERMAN FAIR.

An advertisement for Whaite's German Fair in Bridge
Street, Manchester in 1879. It was a beautifully decorated
toyshop specializing in automata, clockwork models and
wooden German 'penny' novelties

on the face of Raymond, our five-year-old cousin, as he sat on Santa's warm lap happily recounting all he'd like for Christmas: 'A battleship, a clockwork train, a whip an' top, a Spitfire, a fort, some lead soldiers . . .' The list went on and on, endlessly, until at last Uncle managed to coax him away with the promise of a fish and chip tea in the store's cafeteria.

After leaving the warm sanctuary of Lewis's wonderland, we had just turned into Corporation Street on the way back to Victoria when Raymond decided he would like to see Father Christmas just once more before he went home. Faced with the alternatives of a protracted tantrum on one hand or a weary walk back up Market Street on the other, Uncle pondered at length before deciding to take the little lad into one of the stores at the top end of Deansgate, which was slightly nearer and not uphill. After all, he reasoned, Raymond wouldn't know the difference.

It didn't take long to find a store with a Father Christmas, and Raymond's expression of delight when he saw the old gentleman's bewhiskered smile through a chink in the grotto fabric made it all worth while. 'Come up here, son,' said Father Christmas, beckoning with one hand and patting his knee with the other. And then, giving the lad a hug, he asked: 'And what would you like me to bring you for Christmas?'

Raymond regarded him sternly until, in his best Rossendale accent, came the only possible response to such a query: 'Tha's bloody soon fergeet, an't ti?'

T' Nativity Play

There is a special magic about the weeks before the Christmas holidays at infants' and junior schools. If half the battle of education lies in capturing the children's imagination, then what teacher could fail to make the most of a time when cutting out paperchains and snowmen and singing well-loved songs can be at the heart of the learning process? They did not make a great song and dance about Christmas at my primary school, but I still have the most vivid memories of sticking sweet-paper jewels on golden crowns and singing of feathery snowflakes falling in the winter George VI died.

Nativity plays passed me by completely as a child, as they did many people of my generation. But they have been around for decades in some schools, and today they seem to be an almost universal part of end-of-term festivities. I can identify with both of these little poems – and 'Stage Struck' is a cheering reminder that while the pattern of family life has changed, in Lancashire as elsewhere, the county still abounds in tight-knit communities in which Nanas and Grans make up half the audience of the school nativity play!

Stage Struck

'Nana,' Sarah sed t' me,
(Near seven years o' age)
'D' y' think as Miss'll pick mi
T' act on t' Christmas stage?'

· A Lancashire Christmas ·

Ah lukked at 'er – aw luvvin' –
'Aye – if oo feels tha's able . . .
Wot part ud y' geet i' mind?'
Oo answered: 'Gangel Abriel'.

Mary Marcroft

Sayin' Mi Piece

When t' teycher said: 'We'll do a play,'
Ah knew Ah'd ged a part –
Ah allus did like dressin' up,
Ah know mi piece bi heart.

The grand finale: a nativity play at Sacred Heart Infant
School at Hindsford, Tyldesley, in 1972

· A Lancashire Christmas ·

In t' fost scene we're on t' mountainside,
An' Ah'm a shepherd boy,
Then th' angel comes an' tells us
Of good tidin's of great joy.

An' th' angel's ar Elizabeth Ann,
Oo does look weel wi' wings,
An' one o' Mam's owd cotton sheets
Teed up wi' tinsel strings.

We 'ed a practice yesterday,
We couldn't ged it reet,
Ah hit one lad wi' t' lantern
For stan'in' on mi feet.

Ar teycher played t' piano,
So we sang a carol then,
An' Mary coom wi' Joseph,
An' after, t' Three Wise Men.

They'd cardboard crowns, an' browt their gifts
For Mary an' her Son,
That's when Ah 'ed t' say mi piece:
'God bless us, every one'.

Josephine Iddon

from

Look Back With Love

DODIE SMITH

Dodie Smith, a prolific writer best remembered today for her play Dear Octopus *and her children's book* The Hundred and One Dalmatians, *was born in White-field, near Manchester, in 1896 and spent her early childhood in the Old Trafford area of the city; that is the scene of these reminiscences from her 1974 childhood autobiography. At the turn of the century Old Trafford was a leafy suburb for the comfortably-off, and Dodie Smith's memories of her youth in Manchester contrast sharply with those of many of her contemporaries. In due course she went off to school in London, and later to RADA, and one might have thought that her career in the glamorous inter-war theatre world might have expunged all thoughts of the North from her mind. Far from it; seventy years on, recollections of curl-rags and calling-cards and nights of anticipation and deflation flooded back as if they were yesterday . . .*

By the Christmas of 1904 I was a fully-fledged party-goer. The

invitations, with fancy decorations, usually said: 'We are giving a little party and would so much like to see you there'. If, at the bottom, it was '3 till 8 o'clock' it was a babies' party. '4 to 9' was better and '5 to 10' was bliss. And there were a few glorious invitations on plain gilt-edged cards which said 'Dancing, 6 to 11'. I was never allowed to stay till eleven, but even to possess one of these almost grown-up cards made one feel mature.

The thrill of a party began the night before, when my mother took special care over putting my hair in curl-rags. Every curl that was not quite tight enough was done again, and I did not complain if the tightness was uncomfortable; it was part of the excitement. I cannot now imagine how I managed to sleep with those hard knobs, like glossy chestnuts from each of which sprouted a flutter of white curl-rag, all over my head. Next day time hung heavily until the afternoon when, on being told by my mother that everything was ready, I would steal upstairs, open the bedroom door very quietly,

Provisions for gentlefolk: the staff line up amid the
Christmas display at Seymour Mead's in Urmston,
Manchester in the 1920s

and gloat. The fire would be burning brightly and on the bed
would be my party dress (always pink chiffon), a pink cloth
hooded cape, a white wool shawl to go over it, bronze slippers,
white silk openwork stockings, white silk mittens and a choice
of three fans – ostrich feather, hand-painted or lace. On the
dressing-table white corals, a very small diamond heart on a
pink ribbon and a pearl-set swastika on a narrow golden chain
awaited my selection.

My mother was never too hard-up to afford cabs for my
parties, into and from which I was carried by the maid who
accompanied me. The drive there was the high spot of my
evening, for anticipation soared; the drive back was very
different for never, never did I enjoy parties once I got to
them. No one could discover why I didn't. I was reasonably
popular, I was asked to recite (and did), my dress was admired,
but always when a maid came in to announce 'Miss Dodie

Smith has been called for' (woe betide our maid if she came even five minutes early) my heart sank with the knowledge that the party was over and once again nothing had been quite as I'd hoped – only I didn't know *what* I'd hoped. To this day the smell of tangerines brings back memories of those disillusioning parties: the drawing-room cleared for games with the chairs set round the walls – tidy to start with but gradually becoming littered with paper caps and pulled crackers; the Christmas tree with burnt-out candles – never did I get a present that pleased me; the huge tea where nothing tasted as good as it looked; my desperate effort to enjoy myself, which gradually changed to flat disappointment. Other children seemed blissfully happy – but *I* must have *seemed* happy; I romped and shouted and never ceased to smile, more to encourage myself than out of politeness. So, for all I know, some of the other children may have been discovering how little pleasure there can sometimes be in pleasure.

I have retained a dislike for large numbers of people gathered together hell-bent on enjoying themselves, but I doubt if my disappointment over children's parties was early evidence of this. I believe it was mainly caused by my envy of older girls who received attentions from boys in their teens; for at eight years old I already had a longing for romance and was attracted by boys at least five years older than I was, who did not even know I existed. During the first hours of parties there were boisterous games such as hunt the slipper, blind man's buff, nuts in May – game of ignominy for me, for children far smaller than I was could pull me across; but after tea there were kissing games, shy widow, turn and trencher and, most popular of all, postman's knock. I was chosen often enough by little boys, but never did glorious young men of thirteen or fourteen thump on the door and demand my presence in the hall, where the lights were turned low and giggling maids hid in dim kitchen passages to watch the fun.

The Christmas Card Scene

JIM BURNS

The Poet Burns in this case is Jim of that ilk, born in Preston in 1936 and one of the most original voices in contemporary British poetry for two decades or more. His work has been published widely in Britain and overseas, and his enduring love–hate relationship with his home town has been examined in depth by almost all the newspapers and magazines that care about poetry. This poem comes from his second major collection, The Goldfish Speaks From Beyond The Grave, *published in 1976.*

Well, I arrive home from work,
and waiting for me is a Xmas card
from a friend. 'Write a poem,'
he says, 'about the scene
on the front of this card.'
Christ, I'm tired and wet, and
worried about the economic state
of the nation, and he wants me
to write poems. And about a scene
that can't be true! I mean,
whoever saw such idyllic snow?
Try walking through it to get to

the house, and you'll find
that your feet are soon soaking,
and the wind slices in from those
pretty hills across the lake.
What's more, if you ever arrive,
they'll frown, and say, 'How nice
of you to come so unexpectedly,
don't mind the central-heating,
it isn't working, and we'd give you
a whisky, but George drank it all
last night, didn't you darling?'
I imagine all this as I look
at the card, and I realise I can't
leave my footprints across its
smooth, well-ordered whiteness.

Kisses for the Weavers

JEAN SEDMAN

Anyone who was a bit slow-thinking was often put in the mill as a 'reacher-in'. This job consisted of helping the men in the preparation room, where the warps were made. It was very

First-footing: doublers let their hair down at the
J. Nicholls' Mill at Newton Heath, Manchester

boring, but quite a good way of earning a living for youngsters who were not quite the brightest. They were treated very kindly by the folks in the mill, and always had a special treat at Christmas.

One lad at my dad's mill had a thing about owning certain objects. He used to go to the local slipper baths for his weekly bath, and the attendant always drew the required amount of hot water and then left you to get on with it. After that, no more hot water could be drawn; you'd had your share!

This lad's ambition was to have his own bath key, so he could turn on and have some more hot water after the attendant had gone. His chance came one week when the attendant forgot, and left the bath key in place when he went away. Our canny lad pinched it; it was his trophy, to be shown to everyone in the mill that week. Fancy – he could now turn the water on and off at will! He was a king! Another ambition of his was to own what he called a 'rate machine' – the machine at the town hall that stamped the official receipt when you paid your house rates.

At Christmas time the young lads would go round with mistletoe kissing the older women weavers. The lads would collect a shilling from each weaver they kissed, and could make quite a bit of spare pocket money. The most marvellous parties would be held in the mill, either at breakfast time or ten or fifteen minutes before stopping time. The workers, of course, had this amount docked from their wages. Quite often at Christmas, too, instead of brewing your own tea, the loom-sweeper would brew for the whole mill and carry it round in his bucket, pouring out to each weaver with a ladle. In later years I remembered the tea I'd swigged at these dos when I visited dad at work – and I recollect with horror, now, that part of the loom-sweeper's duties was to clean out the loos. As far as I can recall, he owned only the one bucket. Still, I've lived to tell the tale.

Christmas with Wonnie

DIANA ALEXANDER

For me, a little of the light went out of Christmas when my grandfather was no longer there to revel in it. Born when

Queen Victoria still had nearly 20 years to reign, he often reminded us proudly that he started work in Preston on the first day of the new century. He died just a few miles farther down the Ribble, at Lytham, at the end of the 1960s.

Wonnie, the nickname by which his children and grandchildren affectionately knew him, was a larger-than-life character. During the Second World War, when he patrolled the Ribble beaches as a member of the Home Guard, people used to remark on his resemblance to the hero of the hour, Winston Churchill. In the family we felt that Mr Pickwick was nearer the mark. Whichever of those colourful personalities you chose, Wonnie shared with them the view that you got out of life what you put into it — especially at Christmas.

Long before the great day he would entertain us with his favourite secular carol, which went:

> *Get up, old wives,*
> *And bake your pies,*
> *It's Christmas Day in the morning.*
>
> *The bells will ring,*
> *The cats will sing,*
> *And the dogs will go to church.*
> *Some in rags,*
> *Some in tags,*
> *And some in ruffled shirts.*

I have never heard this sung outside Lancashire, but years later I found it in a book of old carols, and couldn't help shedding a tear. At the time, it never failed to delight me and to irritate my busy grandmother, who had heard it so many times before.

But perhaps we should expect to be irritated by the ones we love at Christmas — and, in later life, look back and wish that they were still around to put our backs up. A friend recalls his

father, who was born in Swinton, Manchester and brought up
not far away at Simister, having two very typically Lancashire
Christmas catchphrases.

Every year after Christmas dinner he would pronounce:
'Well, if everyone's fared as well as us today, they won't have
done so bad.' My friend agrees that, on the face of it, this
seems a perfectly worthy sentiment, but confesses that it drove
him to distraction as a child. 'We weren't particularly well off,
but we weren't poor, either,' he recalls. 'Somehow this phrase
seemed to put us at the bottom of the heap, and make us the
lowest common denominator. I remember when I was about
six I used to think well, why *shouldn't* some people have fared
worse than us? I don't think I could have been a very nice kid.'

The other phrase could be relied upon to surface regularly at
around nine o'clock on Christmas Day evening; the tea of cold
capon was over and the pots were washed, but festive thoughts
were still in the children's minds, some toys were yet unplayed
with and there were selection boxes still to be opened. 'Well,'
father would say, getting up to wind the clock, 'it's as far away
as ever, now.' In other words, that's it, back to reality.
Looking back, my friend realises that both phrases must have
harked back to his father's childhood, pronounced at around
the time of the First World War by aunties and uncles brought
up in the mill towns and Manchester suburbs of Victorian
days. But his recognition of their social history today does not
make his feelings about them any less irksome.

As for my grandfather, being a devout Christian and a
confirmed epicurean, he very definitely regarded Christmas
Day as the highspot of his year. In the morning he would swell
the choir of St Cuthbert's, Lytham, with his fine bass voice –
one so fine that when he grew too infirm to walk to church, the
choirmaster would send a taxi to fetch him.

Then it was lunchtime, and Wonnie's Christmas dinner was
a family joke. He tried something of everything, and would

have felt he had failed us if he had not cleared his plate for a second time. We are a family with hearty Lancastrian appetites, but none of us could keep pace with him. 'Could you manage some cheese, Wonnie?' my mother would ask as we all sat back gasping. 'Just a nip, please, dear' — to be followed by a mince pie, and coffee with cream, and yes, a brandy would be very nice, too . . .

Then we would leave him in front of the dining room fire to snooze and snore the afternoon away. But by the early evening he would be tucking in again to cold ham and salad, trifle, Christmas cake, nuts, dates, figs and another nip of his favourite crumbly Lancashire cheese. Finally, my father would escort him home, where he presumably slept the sleep of the just. We often jokingly predicted, in his later years, that his life on this earth would end after just one more Christmas dinner, one more nip . . . In fact he died on St Nicholas Day, and perhaps that was no bad choice, either, for one who came as close as is possible to epitomising the Spirit of Christmases Past, Present and To Come.

A Market for Christmas

In 1985 Raymond Hargreaves published an engrossing portrait of a decade in the life of a Lancashire town in Victorian Years, Bolton 1850–1860. *His narrative,*

covering all aspects of local life, was built up from his extensive study of the Bolton Chronicle *newspaper for those years, and his policy of quoting reports verbatim gives us a true flavour of the times. In this first excerpt from his book we are taken back to the* Chronicle *of 22 December 1855, and an article titled 'Opening of the Bolton New Market Hall'. Today the hall, painstakingly refurbished, stands at the heart of a new shopping complex.*

Bolton, within the last few years, has risen greatly in population, wealth and importance, and so rapidly have its material improvements succeeded each other that a stranger who knew the town 20 years ago would now scarcely be able to recognise it. New churches, new institutions, public offices and a new bank rival each other in taste and architectural display, and the new and splendid Market Hall, whose public opening we record below, crowns the whole with classic purity and magnificence. In point of utility no building ever supplied a greater public want, while as an ornament to the town it stands unsurpassed.

The Opening Ceremony

At an early hour on Wednesday morning the sounds of the church bells pealed merrily through the air, and flags which floated from all the buildings and many of the shops in the principal streets indicated that the day was to be one of general rejoicing. The weather was all that could be desired. A number of shops were wholly and others partially closed, and some of the mills and workshops ceased working early to allow such hands as were desirous of joining in the public procession in honour of the opening an opportunity to do so. The various societies and bands of music intending to join in the procession began to form near the Borough Court at 12 o'clock.

· A Lancashire Christmas ·

The *Bolton Almanack's* view of the Market Hall when it
opened for Christmas, 1885

The Market Hall by Gaslight

The Market Hall was crowded with people from soon after six
o'clock to ten o'clock. It was brilliantly lit up. The Gilnow
Saxhorn band occupied the platform; many people had gone
there in the hope of enjoying a dance, but the building was so
crowded that dancing was out of the question.

The Ball

A grand ball in celebration of the opening was held in the
evening at the Bath's Assembly Rooms, and was attended by
the elite of the town and neighbourhood.

The first market in the hall was held on Saturday, and it
being the Christmas market, there was an excellent show of all
descriptions of poultry. The butchers soon disposed of their
choice cuts at $7\frac{1}{2}$d. a pound. The show of Christmas geese was
very meagre, but such as were in the market sold readily at 8d.
a pound.

At night the hall was so crowded that the avenues were
almost impassable, and during this time several pockets were
picked.

Christmas at the Mill House

ELIZABETH K. BLACKBURN

In two books of reminiscences, Elizabeth Blackburn painted a vivid picture of an East Lancashire childhood in the Edwardian and First World War era. She lived at the Mill House in Aqueduct Road, Blackburn, and it was indeed the mill that dominated her family's life. From her book When I was a Little Girl, *these are her memories of Christmas 1915.*

Christmas has come, and there is no sign of the war ending, as people said it would do at Christmas; but we manage to have a little celebration in the mill on the day before Christmas Eve with the kissing money we get during the week. This is a very old custom, when the braver women weavers and big girls go round the mill and kiss all the men from Uncle John, the manager, to the youngest man weaver, and get some money from them. This is then spent on pies and cakes and coffee, which we eat at our looms wearing paper caps and singing Christmas carols, which can be heard over the clatter of the looms. It is quite a merry time.

Christmas Day is on a Saturday this year so we only get a half-day for it, although Uncle John stops the engine early Friday afternoon to give the women time off for shopping.

· A Lancashire Christmas ·

This simply-written account gives us a true insider's view of mill life nearly eighty years ago – the grumbling over the fact that Christmas Day was a half-day Saturday, and the boss's well-meaning attempt to give the girls a couple of hours off for shopping on the Friday afternoon. As this excerpt from Elizabeth Blackburn's book In and Out the Windows *shows, the half-day controversy was far more than simply a good-natured grouse, even if you did have relatives in high places.*

Following the August holiday the next break was Christmas, but after the 1914–18 war we had a short September break of two days, when it always seemed to rain. Christmas was a most welcome holiday . . . We really longed for another day's rest after the festivities, and also an extra day at New Year.

Just before Christmas a large parcel would arrive from my mother's family, containing simple presents – a large pork pie, a number of mince pies and our yearly stock of homoeopathic medicines from a chemist uncle. If I got half a chance I would nick a few of these sugar-coated pills, which tasted as good as sweets, but I never suffered any ill effects.

Our Christmas, and that of our neighbours, was spent quietly, a bit of extra sleep, some good food and drink – a few might get drunk, but not many – and, as Mammie Eccles expressed it, 'the joy of putting your feet up'.

The Mill House was a very cold house, and one of the luxuries of Christmas was a fire in the bedroom on Christmas Eve. I still remember going to sleep in the warmth of it as I watched the shadows dancing on the wall and over the flowered text which read: 'For Thou Lord Only Makest Me To Dwell In Safety'. It was a text which comforted a childhood fear of the dark, and which remained with me as a Factory Inspector, with the hope that our work of administering industrial safety laws might be giving the Lord a bit of help!

Christmas presents were few and simple and could be

contained in the stocking hung up at the bottom of the bed, an apple and an orange, a few sweets – and, to my great joy, a book. On Christmas Eve the church and chapel carollers came round, and during Christmas morning the Salvation Army band and singers greeted us with hymns and carols. The day ended with early bed after all the excitement, with a six o'clock start as usual on Boxing Day for the factory workers. The Christmas holiday was all too short, and I remember Polly and me weeping when Christmas fell on a Saturday in 1915 and we only got half a day's holiday that year.

The Christmas Bombings

JAMES EDWARD HOLROYD

My father spent most of the Second World War in the Army stationed in central London, and he had as much first-hand experience of blitzes and bombings as anyone you could meet. In spite of all that he remained remarkably tolerant of Old Jerry and his aerial activities – until he looked back on the Christmas of 1940, and the Luftwaffe's *devastation of his beloved Manchester. Cross Street Chapel, the Assize Courts, the Royal Exchange, the Market Place . . . as a postman in Civvy Street he knew*

every square yard of the old city, and he mourned the blows
dealt to those buildings and so many others.

I was reminded of the Assize Courts in the spring of
1990, when inmates wreaked havoc on Strangeways
Prison. The ruins of the old court buildings, on Bury New
Road next to the gaol, were allowed to stand for a few
years after the war, and it struck me that the prisoners
had done almost as thorough a job on the one as Hitler had
on the other. This account of the bombings is by a man
who, as a Ministry of Information press officer, had a
perhaps unique insight into events in the city over those
frightening few days fifty years ago.

In the morning newspapers of December 23rd, 1940,
Liverpool was named as having been bombed for the third
night running. But in the same issues, accounts of the massive
blitz on Manchester the previous night had to label the city
anonymously as 'an inland town in North-west England'. Still
blazing fiercely, the Royal Exchange could be referred to only
as 'a commercial building'.

These news restrictions were part of the Government's
censorship policy of not revealing to the enemy names either of
localities or individual buildings until it was established that
the Germans had identified them. Liverpool had already been
repeatedly attacked and named in enemy communiqués.
Manchester had not.

On Monday afternoon, it was decided that key staff of the
Ministry of Information should stay the night at their base just
across the road from the Royal Exchange. I grabbed a few buns
from the Lyons tea shop round the corner. Sirens sounded as
we took a couple of camp-beds down to the basement of the
Manchester Guardian building in Cross Street, from which we
operated.

As press officer to the Ministry, I had a corner where all

the national press had installed their direct telephone lines. In the intervals between dealing with calls — if there were any intervals that night — one heard the thuds of high explosives.

The reality of the bombing was given a close personal note by the arrival of James Pilkington, the MOI night-duty officer, and his wife. Their home had been destroyed the previous night. He had put out a number of incendiary bombs in Albert Square on the way in, and his wife was able to snatch a few hours' sleep on one of the two camp-beds.

John R. Scott, head of the *Guardian* and MOI chief regional officer, appeared from time to time, wearing a civilian tin hat. He had been helping the MG team of firewatchers, who had sand-bagged or kicked off the roof numerous incendiary bombs

Market Place in Manchester, Christmas 1940. On the left is the half-timbered Wellington Inn, which survived this ordeal and was preserved with no costs spared when post-war redevelopment transformed its surroundings

The Christmas party at Regent Road School in 1946, which
also celebrated its reopening after the Manchester blitzes

that could have destroyed the building. Although then over
60, he was as excited as a schoolboy. 'Cross Street Chapel has
just gone up!' he told us on one flying visit. Mrs Scott was
doubtless aware of his impetuous streak; more than once
during the night she telephoned from Fallowfield for reassur-
ance that he was not taking undue risks.

What we did not know was that throughout the threat of
invasion in 1940 he had carried a £30,000 emerald necklace in
his pocket, having been advised to try to escape if the Germans
landed. During that summer the authorities had proposed
putting a military guard on the *Guardian* office, but stubborn
individualist that he was, Scott wouldn't agree to it.

At about 1.30 a.m. on Tuesday the all-clear sounded, and I
climbed a vertical internal ladder to the MG roof. A never-to-
be-forgotten Christmas Eve had been ushered in by a city

ringed anew with fire. The Royal Exchange opposite, and Woolworth's beyond, were still burning, as were the much-loved Victoria Buildings with their sequence of Aesop's fables carved in stone. The Market Place area – that remaining bit of city history – was an inferno, to be destroyed completely save for the miraculous preservation of the old Wellington Inn block.

Eastward, the fires around Miller Street, Cannon Street and the Assize Courts were aglow, while to the south the line of great warehouses around Piccadilly still flamed against the night sky. The failure of a number of firms to provide an efficient service of firewatchers on their buildings brought a warning from the MOI that this legal obligation would in future be enforced rigorously. Stepping out of the office for a breath of air on the afternoon of Christmas Eve, I saw a soldier on guard outside Lewis's shattered windows to prevent looting . . .

Amazingly, the transport department reported that not a single tram had been destroyed. The chamber of commerce quickly established a committee to help firms whose premises had been rendered unusable. The enormous floor of the Royal Exchange was wrecked and lay open to the sky, but within 16 weeks emergency repairs enabled it to function again. Meanwhile, beneath the reeking pall of smoke, subdued Christmas celebrations went on; *Robinson Crusoe* was at the Palace, Sargent conducted the Hallé's *Messiah* at the Odeon . . .

from

Willy's Grave

EDWIN WAUGH

Edwin Waugh of Rochdale (1817–90) was a superstar of Lancashire dialect writing in Victorian times. His early songs in standard English made no great impact, but he hit the jackpot in 1856 with Come Whoam, *a tear-jerking broadsheet ballad with a happy ending – if you consider a drunken slob's decision to reinflict himself on his wife and children to add up to a happy ending.*

From then on, Waugh flourished both in his writing and as a performer of his verses, and by 1860 he was working at his art full-time; the son of a shoemaker, he had previously held various jobs in the printing and book trades and in schools' administration. The esteem he enjoyed in later life is demonstrated clearly by the fact that when he fell sick in 1881 he was granted a civil list pension of £90 a year for life.

Willy's Grave *is a product of his late years, the early 1880s. It is a near-contemporary of George R. Sims's* Christmas Day in the Workhouse, *but in spirit it is much closer to another Sims epic,* Billy's Rose – *a great favourite with magic lantern audiences on cold winter nights; both poems paint pictures of harrowing poverty, and end with the image of tiny frozen bodies lying in or under the snow.*

I include Willy's Grave — *with just two repetitive verses deleted — to give some insight into the kind of tales they were telling each other round the fireside at Christmas a hundred years ago. Some Victorian ballads were scarcely sentimental at all, the tough and trenchantly damning* Christmas Day in the Workhouse *being a case in point. And as for the likes of* Willy's Grave *and* Billy's Rose, *I believe writers would be doing a brisk trade in them to this day if our babies and toddlers were still dying all around us.*

The frosty wind was wailing wild
Across the moorland wold.
The cloudless vault of heaven was bright
With studs of gleaming gold.
The weary cotter's heavy lids
Had closed with closing day;
And on his silent hearth a tinge
Of dying fire-light lay.

No footsteps trod the tiny town,
The drowsy street was still,
Save where the wandering night-wind sang
Its requiem wild and shrill.
The stainless snow lay thick upon
Those quaint old cottage eaves;
And wreaths of fairy frost-work hung
Where grew last summer's leaves.

Icicles hang from the bridge above the frozen stream

· A Lancashire Christmas ·

Each village home was dark and still,
And closed was every door.
For gentle sleep had twined her arms
Around both rich and poor —
Save in one little cot, where by
A candle's flickering ray,
A childless mother sighing sat
And combed her locks of grey.

Her husband and her children all
Were in the last cold bed,
Where one by one she'd laid them down
And left them with the dead.
Then, toiling on towards her rest —
A lonely pilgrim, she —
For God and poverty were now
Her only company.

Upon the shady windowsill
A well-worn Bible lay;
Against the wall a coat had hung
For many a weary day;
And on the scanty table-top,
With crumbs of supper strewn,
There stood, beside a porringer,
Two little empty shoon.

The fire was waning in the grate,
The spinning-wheel at rest,
The cricket's song rang loudly in
That lonely woman's nest
As, with her napkin, thin and worn,
And wet with many a tear,
She wiped the little pair of shoon
Her darling used to wear.

Her widowed heart had often leaped
To hear his prattle small,
He was the last that she had left —
The dearest of them all.
And as she rocked her to and fro,
While tears came dreeping down,
She sighed and cried: 'Oh, Willy, love —
These little empty shoon!'

With gentle hand she laid them by,
She laid them by with care;
For Willy he was in his grave,
And all her thoughts were there.
She paused before she dropped the sneck
That closed her lambless fold,
It grieved her heart to bar the door
And leave him in the cold.

A threadbare cloak she happed around
Her limbs, so thin and chill;
She left her lonely cot behind,
While all the world was still;
And through the solitary night
She took her silent way,
With weeping eyes towards the place
Where little Willy lay.

The pallid moon had climbed aloft
Into the welkin blue,
A snow-clad tree across the grave
Its leafless shadow threw.
And as that mournful mother sat
Upon a mound thereby
The bitter wind of winter sighed
To hear her lonely cry.

'My little Willy's cowd an' still —
He's not a word for me!
T' last tiny leaf has dropt away
Fro this owd withered tree!
Oh, my poor heart! He's gone! He's gone!
Aw'm lonely under t' sky!
He'll never clip my neck again,
An' tell me not to cry!

He's crept into his last dark nook
An' laft me pinin' here!
An' never-moor his two blue e'en
For me mun twinkle clear!
He'll never say his prayers again,
At his poor mammy's knee!
Oh, Willy, oh, Aw'm lonely now!
When mun Aw come to thee?'

The snow-clad yew tree stirred with pain
To hear that plaintive cry;
The old church listened, and the spire
Still pointed to the sky.
With kindlier touch the wintry wind
Played in her locks of grey;
And the queenly moon, upon her head,
Shone with a softened ray.

She rose to leave that lonely bed,
Her heart was grieving sore;
One step she took, and then her tears
Fell faster than before.
She turned and gave another look —
One lingering look she gave —
Then, sighing, left him lying in
His little snowy grave.

Flying Feathers

KAY DAVENPORT

Kay Davenport, brought up in Preston and now living in Rochdale, has written prolifically about her girlhood memories in recent years. This story and a second one in this anthology, 'Childhood Christmas of Magic', come from her 1989 collection A Lancashire Hotch Potch. *Her motivation for putting her reminiscences on paper is made plain in the dedication in that book, which reads simply: To my grandchildren, with love.*

My mother was a firm believer in the saying that God would provide – especially at Christmas. And in spite of the many calls He must have had for help from Lancashire folk in the late Twenties, more often than not her faith was justified. She never did much Christmas shopping or bought the Christmas dinner, for the Lord did indeed frequently provide it – or at least, He must have had a heavenly hand in the many raffles my father supported. Our draw tickets would come home to roost, along with the poor birds which were, by then, past the roosting stage – or, indeed, any stage at all.

Sometimes father would win a piece of meat, and I remember one such lump of purplish beef on our willow-pattern plate, looking for all the world like the chops of an apoplectic old man. Its fat was as yellow as banana skin – and just as tough. More often there would be a red-brown hen or a dirty white goose hanging from a hook under our back kitchen shelf. The eyes would be glazed, the poor beak agape, wings flopped open, a sorry sight. Dressed it was not, and I could never understand how a bird, fully clothed in a million feathers, was called 'not dressed'. I was always sorry to see a goose suspended by its feet, for that meant we would get our chests rubbed with revolting goose-grease should we fall ill with a chesty cough. Just thinking of the grease was enough to keep one well. We children had the task of pulling out the reluctant feathers, and as the birds were seldom freshly killed when we received them, this was a horrible and daunting task. Brown or white feathers flew in clouds about the small kitchen, which smelled so strongly of paraffin . . . Our fat fox-terrier, wildly excited by the flying feathers, barked loudly and rushed round in ever-decreasing circles. My elder brother would make me scream in terror as he cut off the bird's feet and, by pulling the stringy sinews tight, made the claws open and close. He used to chase me all over the house to scratch the tender nape of my neck or my bare knees with the ghastly yellow feet.

Once we won a Christmas cake and a bottle of red wine from the local convent. Two nuns brought the prizes round, and their encounter with my Baptist mother must have astonished them as well as her when she opened our front door to them. She presented a startling picture. She had been dozing by the fire and the nuns, in their long black habits and looming in our shadowy porch, surprised her sleepy mind so that she mumbled incoherently at them. She in her turn must have been a bizarre sight to the holy women. She often wore her hat indoors when the weather was cold, believing that a warm head helped to keep the rest of her cosy. She would put on her hat when going upstairs to make the beds, for there was no central heating, then, only the one fire in the living room. Our canary often perched on the brim of her black hat, or took a promenade around it. He was particularly fond of the little bunch of bluish feathers that decorated it, probably thinking it to be a kindred soul. Perhaps he was lonely.

On the day the nuns called he was in his favourite position, and mother wondered why their eyes were turned piously upwards until, glancing sideways in our hall mirror, she saw the reflection of herself and the contented, nestling bird. This close encounter of my small mother and the stately, delicately-featured nuns makes a lovely remembered picture. I remember, too, the rich cake, all covered with almond paste, which they said they had baked themselves. Dad got into trouble with mother later for suggesting that they had laced it with communion wine. The nuns entered our front parlour bearing the prizes, and sat down to talk. Their faces fascinated me, one so old and wrinkled, the other so young and sweet. The flowing garment of the younger one cascaded in graceful folds around our three-legged stool. I sat there thinking that my friend Hilda, who attended a convent school, had assured me that nuns actually wore corsets. She had felt the whalebone as one of the younger ones had bent down to help her in class. Nuns, to me, were as beings from another world. These two stayed quite a while, and mother was running out of small-talk. Fortunately, dad came home, and seeing the collecting box to hand, he realised that a donation would be welcome. So the gracious nuns departed with many blessings, probably thinking that mother was in need of a few – not to mention our short-sighted canary.

Later, the Christmas bird had been plucked, and father had set the shelf paper alight as he singed the last recalcitrant feathers and down from the poor, cold fowl. My brother had received a thick ear, and I had not been able to find any hidden presents. My doll's leg had come off at the thigh, exposing a piece of elastic and a hook where a dimpled pot leg should have been. Then it was time for bed, and the reciting of prayers with hope for a well-filled pillowcase. I hadn't been forgotten, and on Christmas morning I found it at the bottom of my bed, bulging nicely. I was a bit puzzled as I felt the shapes in the early dawn light. My brother had been up to his tricks again, and had padded out the bag with a large white loaf. But there were other items as well as the obligatory sugar pig and the little gold net of silver paper-wrapped chocolate pennies. Not so many things, for the Twenties were not roaring for working-class families; but then again, we didn't expect much, so we were not disappointed.

Christmas Blackmail

PHOEBE HESKETH

Born in Preston in 1909 and most closely associated with the moorland-edge village of Rivington, her home for decades, Phoebe Hesketh has been one of the most prolific of Britain's post-war poets. Her work has won favour with the whole spectrum of the poetry-reading public, from browsers through popular magazines to the most stringent

and demanding critics, but she has never courted personal publicity. Perhaps this is one reason why her output has been 'absurdly underrated', according to the reviewer and editor Al Alvarez; that having been said, the honest strength of her poetry is now well enough known to ensure that it will not be forgotten. This lament over Christmas charity mail is one of her later works, published in her collection Preparing to Leave *in 1977.*

Like early snow they come
spirits of advent
through letter-box and door –
a sort of blackmail
in these dumb appeals.
How shall we choose
between the blind, lame, deaf and those
hungry eyes of children hammering
our hearts till nails
are driven through?

Confused, we turn to go, assailed
by other cries:
Save the Whale, Gorilla, Kangaroo!

Carols in the Wards

Looking forward, counting off the weeks, that's as much a part of Christmas to a child as the great day itself. It was to me, anyway, and from the time I was eight the fourth Sunday of Advent was a beacon to signal that the wait would soon be over. I had joined the choir of All Saints' Church at Stand, north of Manchester, in the May of 1954, and as summer turned into autumn it became clear even to us smallest boys that Christmas would be a little more special than usual this year.

The recently arrived choirmaster, Mr Middleton, had brought with him a tradition of carolling in the wards of Crumpsall Hospital on the afternoon of the last Sunday before Christmas. The evening of that day was already marked down for the church's main carol service, the one time in the calendar when there was not a spare pew to be had. For the next ten years the hours between 2 and 8 p.m. on that Sunday were among the most hectic, stimulating and – if, horror of horrors, I had a solo – stressful of my life. In the early years, at least, they were by far the most magical, too.

There grew up a ritual to it all, the watching for the coach turning into Church Lane, the scramble for the back seat, the Christmas tree lights piercing the gloom of the shortest Sunday of the year from the bay windows of Besses and Prestwich. In our attaché cases our surplices lay freshly laundered and starched, our ruffs so stiff and upright that by the end of the evening there would be zig-zags of pink under our chins. In '54 I had not yet qualified for my surplice, in spite of a false alarm, but was allowed to wear one that day by special dispensation. The false alarm came back in early summer after my first choir practice, when my father came to meet me at the vestry door. Mr Middleton was chatting to him in the evening sunshine when suddenly he excused himself and headed for the lockers. 'That's it,' I thought. 'I was so good tonight he's going to come back with my surplice.' Thirty seconds later he re-emerged with a packet of Player's Navy Cut.

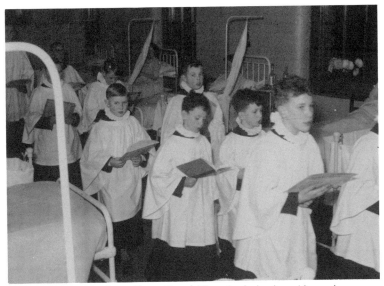

Playing to the gallery: Stand Church choir sings 'Away in a
Manger' in a Crumpsall Hospital maternity ward in 1954

Down at the hospital we would be met by the matron and
taken to a day room to change. Then for the next two hours
our band of two dozen would be swept along through a blur of
corridors of war surplus cream and green, some of them so long
that you could scarcely see their end; we'd pass half-opened
doors of closets smelling of disinfectant and bleach and sick
and gas, hear cries from rooms of pregnant young women and
dying old men, and be jostled by anxious groups in white coats
scudding across the elbow-greased lino. We would send word
about the next ward's carols down the line – '*While Shepherds*
an' *Once in Royal*, pass it on' – and as the afternoon wore on
there would be mutterings from the men at the back about feet
and fags. Outside some wards Mr Middleton would sidle up to
us little ones and say: 'Now, boys, keep your eyes on your
books in here'. So of course we'd gaze around more than ever,

and be rewarded by the sight of old, hollow faces with skin like parchment and eyes upturned in such utter agony that they haunt me still, nearly forty years on. Happier by far were the wards of mothers with their new-born babies, where we would play to the gallery always with *Away in a Manger* and a pretty little Eastern European lullaby known in English as *Rocking*. This lost some of its mystique after 1956, when the likes of Messrs Haley and Presley brought a whole new meaning to that word; meandering along corridors between wards that Christmas a kid called Duncan Patrick aroused mixed reactions by singing it Elvis fashion, complete with those odd little hiccups that seemed to afflict the early rock 'n' roll singers.

As night fell outside the word would go round: 'last one, this, boys'. So we'd give it a little extra gusto, and then stumble along to change and sit down to a meal that never varied from limp chips, lukewarm pork pie and stewed tea. In legend one of the great things about Crumpsall was the slap-up pie and chip nosh afterwards, and you never heard anyone speak ill of it. It was all part of the magic of the day — but I none the less decreed at the age of eight that if that was what passed as grub in hospital, I would never return as anything other than a visitor; so far, touch wood, I have been as good as my word.

We would always be on the last minute on our dash back to church for evensong. One year we were so pressed for time that we changed in the coach, but usually we had five minutes to push through the crowds and tidy up in the Sunday school. Over the years we built up a wide repertoire of carols, but the formula for the opening of the service never varied. Up through the churchyard to the west end, a signal to the deputy organist up in the loft and straight into *Once In Royal David's City*, the first verse sung solo behind the closed inner doors. On the beat of verse two, 'He came down . . .' the sidesmen threw the doors wide and we processed in full voice up the centre aisle, the pews on either side of us ringing with song. In the years since then I have only rarely encountered a church with a greater sense of occasion than Stand. I am still at a loss to know what the tiny Whitefield of Regency times had done to deserve this towering monument to the defeat of Napoleon in 1815, a novice work of the architect of the Houses of Parliament, Charles Barry.

My last Crumpsall Christmas was 1964. I had been away at college for ten weeks, but had been looking forward to it from mid-November, and turned up for practice on the Friday full of festive cheer. 'He can't just waltz back and expect to come in on something like this,' boomed an elderly voice from the bass row. I looked to see the twinkle in the eyes, but there was none. 'Never mind him, you're coming,' said the crucifer Tony Wilding, a big and assertive man young enough to realise that ten years to an eighteen-year-old was all but a lifetime. So I went, and we laughed and sang on the coach, and I knew I'd never be passing that way again.

After evensong that night I met my girlfriend down at the bottom of the dark little vestry path, and we walked along Park Lane in near silence. It was warm and welcoming in the Parkfield pub, though, with a table full of young couples off the new estate beating out *Jingle Bells* with beermats and the juke box blaring the big Christmas hit of that year, the Beatles' *I Feel Fine*. Before too long we were singing along with them. As a spiritual experience it fell short of *In Dulci Jubilo* wafting true and pure around the misty Gothic heights; but I knew the words as well as anyone else, and when the barman filled our glasses there were no inquests about my absence since the early weeks of autumn.

Childhood Christmas of Magic

KAY DAVENPORT

Travelling by bus at Christmas time – all the way from Preston to Leyland for the family Christmas dinner – was an annual ritual not long after the First World War. It was a never-to-be-forgotten experience, well over half a century ago, that journey to Bow Brook House. We might have been going to Leningrad, instead of Leyland, for our Christmas dinner. The excitement was intense as we made preparations to depart from our Frenchwood home before it was properly light, and the lamplighter was still about in Selbourne Street. Having to have our gas mantle glowing in the bedroom gave an unusual impression to the day's start. Christmas stockings had been emptied and the pink sugar pig with its thin string tail had been wrapped in a paper bag for the bus journey.

Would we really travel on a Leyland 'Lion'? Would we see Golden Hill, where dad had been born at the Police Station? Lions and Golden Hills sounded magical, then. So we set off; dad wore his bowler hat, mother her fur tippet with her 'facecloth' coat. I had the task of buttoning up dad's grey spats with the little pearl buttons. I was annoyed because I had to wear my purple felt gaiters which buttoned right up over the knees, and were so stiff that I walked with a slight stagger.

Hazards of winter travel on the upland Manchester Road out
of Burnley in 1913

How I longed for gaiters of soft brown leather like the ones my
friend Alice owned. We set off through the silent early-
morning streets to where we caught the bus at Starchhouse
Square. It was cold in the bus, so I was glad of the despised
gaiters, really, and my yellow woollen gauntlet gloves. I think
the bus must have been the only one to get us to Leyland in the
morning, else why the start from home soon after the crack of
dawn?

It was almost all countryside on the journey, which seemed
endless – misty fields, stark, bare trees, the air frosty, breath
like steam against the cold bus windows. Leyland was really
just a village, mother had said; indeed, dad had once danced
on the village green as a morris man. It was hard to believe

that my pipe-smoking, balding father had tripped lightly on the grass, waving little fancy sticks with bells and ribbons on them, and that he had once dressed in silk breeches and a fancy waistcoat. At grandfather's house in Bow Lane there was a flagged path to the back door where stood a huge water-butt for the rain water for washing woollens. After the cold, the warm kitchen with its big fire and smell of dinner cooking was delicious. Aunts bustled about helping in the buttery and kitchen; uncles didn't help in those days. The house was impressive after our terraced home, and I was a bit in awe of Grandfather Williams. He had been Leyland's first Chief Inspector of Police before he retired, and I could never believe that as a constable he had had his collar ripped by a poacher.

Trouble in Manchester Road, Burnley, near the Bull and Butcher Inn in 1923

Grandma was a small woman who had borne 11 children, all alive and most of them with their families at Bow Brook House for Christmas dinner. All the small fry were packed on low horsehair sofas, very prickly to bare legs – and we mostly found sixpences in the pudding. There were presents from the tree and games, later, but first the men retired to the study to smoke cigars; children were not allowed there without permission, for grown-ups with large families knew what they were about when they wanted peace and quiet. Not that womenfolk got much peace and quiet. There was an inside lavatory beyond the kitchen, and the ladies and little girls had to line up to use it, the only time I've seen a queue for a loo in a private house.

The games were simple: ring-on-a-string, hunt the thimble and musical chairs, a stark contrast to the video and computer games of today. We learned to play bezique at an early age, and I can still feel in memory the chenille of the tablecloth in the sitting room of that Leyland house when we played the game each Christmas. The last time we went there was probably in 1926. I remember going with my parents to catch the bus home, and walking down a Leyland lane with hedges at the sides and the trees bare and ghostly in the fading dusk. A young couple passed us, pushing a wickerwork bassinet, and dad raised his hat as we stepped off the pavement to let them pass. 'Goodnight,' said dad, and they said: 'Goodnight, happy Christmas.'

'Do you know them, dad?' I asked.

'No,' he replied, 'but everyone speaks to everyone else in Leyland.'

A Christmas Barring-Out

In Tudor and Stuart times it was common for the privileged few boys who attended grammar school to play pranks on their masters in the last days before the Christmas holidays. The biggest wheeze of all was to barricade the doors of the schoolhouse, barring out the teachers until they agreed to grant certain holidays and allow the rebels to go unpunished. No doubt, at most schools, this custom developed into a genteel and good-natured ritual – so routine, in fact, that it had died out almost everywhere by early Georgian times.

It lived on in folklore, however – and in the late 1790s, as a last, glorious one-off, it was revived by boys at Ormskirk Grammar School as the ultimate revenge against their headmaster the Revd William Naylor, alias the Flogging Parson. The loathing in which he was held can be judged by the fact that they took the precaution to pack – and use – a blunderbuss and a pistol in defence of their territory.

With no names mentioned, the story was recalled in the Gentleman's Magazine *of 1828, but we now know that the author was Dr Peter Austin Nuttall, the lexicographer who produced* Nuttall's Standard Dictionary *and other reference works. The leader of the escapade can also be*

· A Lancashire Christmas ·

identified – one William Bibby, who was at the school in 1798 and '99. Nuttall described the custom as 'ancient but almost obsolete', and its Ormskirk revival was almost certainly the last of its kind, in Lancashire at least.

Many years had elapsed since the attempt had succeeded; and many times since that period had it been made in vain . . . The scholars had heard of the glorious feats of their forefathers in their boyish years, when they set the lash of the master at defiance for days together. Now, alas, all was changed; the master, in the opinion of the boys, reigned a despot absolute and uncontrolled. The merciless cruelty of his rod and the heaviness of his tasks were insupportable. The accustomed holidays had been rescinded, the usual Christmas feast reduced to a nonentity and the chartered rights of the scholars were continually violated . . . The master was a clergyman of the old school, who for the last 40 years had exercised an authority hitherto uncontrolled, and who had no idea of enforcing scholastic discipline without the exercise of the whip. The consequences of a failure were terrible to reflect upon; but then, the anticipation of success, and the glory attendant upon the enterprise, if successful, were sufficient to dispel every fear.

Bibby, head of the Greek class, soon emerged as the natural leader, quoting tales from the classics to prove that tyrants could fall to the united efforts of determined freedom-fighters. His most urgent message, however, was that the barring-out should go ahead without delay, the next morning:

On a previous occasion, he said, some officious little urchin had told the master the whole plot, several days having been allowed to intervene between the planning of the project and its execution; and to the astonishment of the boys, it appeared they found the master at his desk two hours before the usual time, and had the mortification of being congratulated on their early attendance, with an order to be there every morning at the same hour!'

The following morning, after long hours of plotting and a largely sleepless night, the boys were in the schoolhouse before dawn:

At length the church clock struck eight. 'Proceed to barricade the doors and windows,' exclaimed the Captain, 'or the old lion will be upon us before we are prepared to meet him.' In an instant the old oaken door rang on its heavy hinges. Some with hammers, gimlets and nails were eagerly securing the windows, while others were dragging along the ponderous desks, forms, and everything portable to blockade . . . every place which might admit of ingress. This operation being completed, the Captain mounted the master's rostrum and called over the list of names, when he found only two or three missing . . .

We next commenced an examination of the various weapons, and found them to consist of one old blunderbuss, one pistol, two old swords, a few rusty pokers, and sticks, stones, squibs and gunpowder in abundance. The firearms were immediately loaded with blank powder, the swords were sharpened and the pokers heated in the fire. These weapons were assigned to the most daring company, who had to protect the principal window. The missiles were for the light infantry, and all the rest were armed with sticks.

We now began to manoeuvre our companies by marching them into line and column, so that everyone might know his own situation. In the midst of this preparation the sentinel, whom we had placed at the window, loudly vociferated: 'The parson! The parson's coming!' In an instant all was confusion. Everyone ran he knew not where, as if eager to fly or screen himself from observation. Our Captain instantly mounted a form and called to the captains of the two leading companies to take their stations. They immediately obeyed, and the other companies followed their example, though they found it much more difficult to manoeuvre when danger approached than they had a few minutes before! The well-known footstep which had often struck on our ears with terror was now heard to advance along the portico. The master tried to lift the latch again and again in vain. The muttering of his stern voice sounded on our ears like the lion's growl. A deathlike silence prevailed. We scarcely dared to breathe. The palpitations of our little hearts could perhaps alone be heard. The object of our dread then went round to the front window for the purpose of ascertaining whether anyone was in the school. Every footstep struck us with awe; not a word, not a whisper was heard. He approached close to the window; and with an astonished countenance stood gazing upon us, while we were ranged in battle array, motionless as statues and silent as the tomb. 'What is the meaning of this?' he impatiently exclaimed. But no answer could he obtain, for who would then have dared to render himself conspicuous by a reply? Pallid faces and livid lips betrayed our fears. The courage which one hour before was ready to brave every danger appeared to have fled. Everyone seemed anxious to conceal himself from view, and there would certainly have been a general flight through the back windows had it not been for the prudent regulation of a *corps-de-reserve*, armed with cudgels, to prevent it.

'You young scoundrels, open the door instantly,' he again exclaimed; and what added to our indescribable horror, in a fit of rage he dashed his hand through the window, which consisted of small diamond-shaped panes, and appeared as if determined to force his way in.

Fear and trepidation, attended by an increasing commotion, now possessed us all. At this critical moment every eye turned to our Captain, as if to reproach him for having brought us into this terrible dilemma. He alone stood unmoved, but he saw that none would have courage to obey his commands. Some exciting stimulus was necessary. Suddenly waving his hand, he exclaimed aloud: 'Three cheers for the barring-out, and success to our cause!' Hurra! Hurra! Hurra! The cheers were tremendous. Our courage revived, the blood flushed in our cheeks.

The parson was breaking in; the moment was critical. Our Captain, undaunted, sprang to the fireplace and seized a heated poker in one hand and a blazing torch in the other. The latter he gave to the captain of the sharpshooters, and told him to prepare a volley. Then, with the red-hot poker, he fearlessly advanced to the window seat and, daring his master to enter, he ordered an attack; and an attack indeed was made, sufficiently tremendous to have repelled a more powerful assailant. The missiles flew at the ill-fated window from every quarter. The blunderbuss and the pistol were fired; squibs and crackers, ink stands and rulers, stones and even burning coals came in showers about the casement, and broke some of the panes into a thousand pieces. Blazing torches, heated pokers and sticks stood bristling under the window. The whole was scarcely the work of a minute.

The astonished master reeled back in dumb amazement. He had evidently been struck with a missile or with the broken glass, and probably fancied he was wounded by the firearms. The school now rang with the shouts of 'victory', and continued cheering. 'The enemy again approaches,' cries the Captain. 'Fire another volley; stay; he seeks a parley. Hear him.'

'What is the meaning, I say, of this horrid tumult?'

'The barring-out, the barring-out,' a dozen voices instantly exclaimed.

'For shame,' says he, in a tone evidently subdued. 'What disgrace you are bringing upon yourselves and the school. What will the trustees – what will your parents say? William,' continued he, addressing the Captain. 'Open the door without further delay.'

'I will, Sir,' he replied, 'on your promising to pardon us, and to give us our lawful holidays, of which we have lately been deprived; and not to set us tasks during the holidays.'

'Yes, yes,' said several squealing voices. 'That is what we want – and not to be flogged for nothing.'

'You insolent scoundrels! You consummate young villains!' he exclaimed, choking with rage, and at the same time making a furious effort to break through the already shattered window. 'Open the door instantly, or I'll break every bone in your hides.'

'Not on those conditions,' replied our Captain, with provoking coolness. 'Come on, my boys, another volley.' No sooner said than done – and even with more fury than before. Like men driven to despair, who expect no quarter on surrendering, the little urchins daringly mounted the window seat, which was a broad old-fashioned one, and pointed the firearms and heated poker at him, whilst others advanced with squibs and missiles . . . The master, perceiving their determined obstinacy, turned round without further remonstrance and indignantly walked away.

Relieved from our terrors we now became intoxicated with joy. The walls rang with repeated hurrahs! In the madness of enthusiasm some of the boys began to tear up the forms, throw the books about, break the slates, locks and cupboards, and act so outrageously that the Captain called them to order; not, however, before the master's desk and drawers had been broken open, and every plaything which had been taken from the scholars restored to its owner.'

· A Lancashire Christmas ·

*The boys then set about trying to open an old oak chest
containing the school records with red-hot pokers, but soon
afterwards Naylor returned with a constable, and the
rebels stood around apprehensively as they heard the two
pillars of authority inspecting the damage. What to do?*

Some proposed to drill a hole in the window seat, fill it with
gunpowder and explode it if anyone attempted to enter . . .
Others thought we had better prepare to set fire to the school
sooner than surrender unconditionally.

The affair of the barring-out had now become known, and
persons began to assemble around the windows, calling out
that the master was coming with assistants, and saying
everything to intimidate us. Many of us were completely jaded
with the over-excitement we had experienced since the previous evening. The school was hot, close and full of smoke.
Some were longing for liberty and fresh air, and most of us
were now of the opinion that we had engaged in an affair
which was impossible to accomplish. In this state of mind we
received another visit from our dreaded master. With his stick
he commenced a more furious attack than before, and observ-
ing us less turbulent, he appeared determined to force his way
in, in spite of the barricades. The younger boys thought of
nothing but flight and self-preservation, and the rush to the
back windows became general. In the midst of this constern-
ation our Captain exclaims: 'Let us not fly like cowards. If we
must surrender, let the gates of the citadel be thrown open.
The day is against us, but let us bravely face the enemy, and
march out with the honours of war.' Some few had already
escaped, but the rest immediately ranged themselves on each
side of the school, in two extended lines, with their weapons in
hand. The door was open and the master instantly entered and
passed between the two lines, denouncing vengeance on us all.
But as he marched in, we marched out in military order; and

giving three cheers, we dispersed into the neighbouring fields.

We shortly met again, and after a little consultation it was determined that none of the leaders should come to school until sent for, and a free pardon given. The defection, however, was so general that no corporeal punishments took place. Many of the boys did not return till after the holidays – and several of the elder ones never entered the school again.

War Bonds for Christmas

JAMES EDWARD HOLROYD

'The squat, toad-like war machine, dirty-brown in colour, known as a tank, arrived in Manchester on Saturday night last.' That announcement, in the *Manchester City News* of December 22nd, 1917, shows that such vehicles were still regarded at that time as phenomenal. This one, numbered 113 and affectionately known as Julian, had clattered into Albert Square from Liverpool Road goods station. Installed on the flagstones, it was to be the main attraction and rallying-point in a record week of sales of War Bonds and War Savings Certificates.

· A Lancashire Christmas ·

Because of the need for secrecy no-one was allowed inside the tank, but a separate wooden office had been erected a few yards away, and it was here that long queues began to form from the moment the Lord Mayor stood on top of the unfamiliar monster and declared Tank Week open. No less than £100,000 was taken in the first few minutes.

I can claim a minor vested interest in the event. As a recent arrival with the cotton firm of Greg Brothers and Company of Booth Street, I was given the job of queueing at the hut to purchase certificates which the firm, 150 years old, was presenting to its staff as a patriotic gesture that Christmas.

The certificates were given a special franking to indicate

Call in the tanks? Even in modern times, the snow on the
tops can remind travellers that they can take nothing for
granted in the bleak mid-winter

that they had been bought from the tank, and as a boy I was very excited at being entrusted with this mission. It was fortunate that I was sent to the waiting line early in the week. A day or two later the crowds became so intense that the hut in Albert Square could not cope, and additional receiving points had to be set up along the main corridor of the Town Hall.

On the morning of the tank's arrival the weather was bitter, with showers of sleet and snow; but thousands of Mancunians turned out to see it rumble through the streets, guided by police and escorted by soldiers with fixed bayonets. Hundreds of people walked in front, much in the proprietorial manner of small boys when the band marches resoundingly along the street.

The tank had come to the city from Liverpool, where it had been similarly displayed. No doubt with recollections of the traditional rivalry between 'Liverpool gentlemen and Manchester men', there must have been high jinks in Manchester Town Hall and beyond when it became known early on Friday morning, December 21st, that Liverpool's total of £2,061,012 had been beaten.

The characteristic toughness of Manchester grit and determination then emerged. Stimulated by an appeal from the Lord Mayor to the city's merchant princes, leaders of industry and individual citizens, Manchester gathered its strength and resources in a hurculean effort to eclipse in a single week the total of £3,423,864 which London had subscribed in a fortnight.

By five o'clock on the Friday evening the city had done the trick with a day in hand. No less than £1,750,425 had been subscribed that day alone, to give a magnificent five-day aggregate of £3,755,029.

Bodies of schoolchildren marched to the square to have their certificates stamped. Halton Bank Girls' School in Salford more than doubled membership of its War Savings Association from 200 to 420, and many firms bought thousands of certificates on behalf of employees who would pay by instalments. Details of principal contributions read like a stock exchange list. Lord Dovedale of the Kellner–Partington company came first with £225,000. This was followed by £170,250 from a shareholder of the same company, and not far away, with £100,000 each, were Howard and Bullough, the Co-Operative Wholesale Society and the Lancashire and Yorkshire Railway.

Before going home from the office on that Friday evening I was given another small seasonable commission. In previous years it had been customary for Greg's to provide every member of the staff with a turkey, a goose or a couple of chickens. This largesse, piled high in straw bags or 'basses', had given our little waiting room an air of almost Dickensian jollity. At Christmas 1917, however, all this had been scrapped in favour of War Savings Certificates. All? One of the company's old servants was living in retirement in a bungalow between Bramhall and Cheadle Hulme. It was felt that a small envelope of war certificates, however worthy the cause, might seem a somewhat pallid gift to one who by that time could not have had many more turkeys in prospect. Accordingly, the traditional large bird was somehow secured, and I was given a shilling for rail fare and Saturday morning off in which to deliver it . . .

The Geese Got Fat

SARAH FISHER

The author was looking back some eighty years, to 1890, when this reminiscence was published in 1972. Her family farmed at Hothersall, but the scenes she recalls must have been repeated hundreds of times elsewhere in the countryside around Preston, which was known far and wide for its poultry.

That Christmas my father reared forty geese – more than ever before. On December 23rd he killed them all by sticking. We children – there were seven of us – held the birds whilst he did it so that they bled on to groats, a pint measure being given with each bird sold. The groats were considered a great delicacy; most people added the giblets and cooked them slowly by the fire.

The geese were then carried up to a room above the barn, the plucking room. After their day's work our friends and neighbours came walking or riding horseback through the crisp-cold night air to help prepare the birds for market. This was considered the men's work. They clattered in their clogs up the stairs to the plucking room, seated themselves in a circle and began to pluck, the feathers being piled in the middle. You can imagine the joking, the exchange of news and the good fellowship of this friendly little community.

When the plucking was finished the birds were carried into

Christmas plenty at Paul Webster's butcher's shop in
Burnley Road, Padiham, a century ago in 1890

the house and laid on the great cold stone poultry slab. This is where the ladies took over. They gathered up the feathers for cleaning and ultimate use in beds and cushions; then they fed their menfolk with a huge hot-pot followed by other delicacies, well laced with my mother's home-made wines of many varieties.

When the meal was over my father took each bird and immersed it, first in the bubbling boiler by the roaring fire, and immediately out of this in icy cold water freshly drawn from the pump. I swear that this was the secret of the succulent flesh I enjoyed on fowl when I was a girl – nowhere, alas, to be found today. Next came the drawing and cleaning, and finally each bird, plump, white and neatly trussed, was ready for Preston Market. Only then did our friends leave, mostly to return to their neighbouring farms and start work with the first light.

At 5.30 a.m. on Christmas Eve the trap was brought into the farmyard, freshly scrubbed from top to bottom. Then the goose cloths were brought out, snow-white sheets reserved solely for the purpose and used only at Christmas. The first was laid on the trap floor, then came a layer of geese covered by another cloth and so on, until the trap was full and the final cloth tucked safely over them all.

Bess, the horse, was then brought out and harnessed to the trap. Mother stepped up, took the reins, and off they went to Preston Market, the awesome distance of twelve miles. When they arrived the first job was to stable Bess at the now long gone York Hotel in Church Street, where the landlord was James Bonney. The Christmas fare was then removed from the trap into huge market baskets, each with its goose cloth. These had then to be carried to the Public Hall, but boys from seven years of age upwards were available to do the job for a few Christmas coppers.

My mother had her own pitch in the Public Hall, as had all

the farmers' wives, so they were known to their regular customers. When all the geese were sold some of the baskets were refilled with household necessities, after which my mother returned to the York Hotel, harnessed up the horse, reloaded the trap and set off for home. She always told us that Bess didn't need any driving; with head high and hooves flying, she made it back with no guidance.

When I said mother filled her baskets with household necessities, that was not the whole story. I still treasure, eighty years on, some of the gifts and trinkets she also found time to buy – and I remember the sight of her and Bess returning home from market as one of the highlights of our Christmas on the farm.

from

On the Pig's Back

BILL NAUGHTON

The novelist Bill Naughton, perhaps best known for Alfie, *was a Bolton lad of resolutely Irish stock. In this extract from his recently published childhood memoir he looks back to the early 1920s, and a Christmas Eve that*

helps to convince him that his folks are a very different breed from their neighbours all around. A few paragraphs earlier he confesses: 'I cannot get away from a feeling that underneath all the fuss and merry-making, Christmas is a sad time. The odd thing is that no Christmas comes in the next sixty years without a sense of that same lonely, sad, and unfulfilled feeling. After all, wasn't it a sorry end in store for that babe in the manger — or so it must have seemed to the Holy Mother?'

The atmosphere is warming up, but there is no drinking just yet. My father comes in, and after giving his loud, awkward welcomes to everyone, he lets out grunts of pleasure and thanks at the sight of all the bottles of whiskey on the table. By gum, I'm thinking to myself, we must be a rich family. I'll bet there's not a house in the neighbourhood can brag of that much whiskey on the table on Christmas Eve. Father now brings out the whiskey from the Foudys, for he's going to let these Micks from the country see that he has influential friends in the town — and is not just the shopboy they take him for. The trouble with him — apart from his animosity — is the intensity with which he expresses everything he feels; there is no lightness of touch, rarely a waggish remark, but a fierce seriousness, except when he raises the special bottle of Jameson, to read the label, and then his manner is solemn, and his voice sinks into a pious hoarseness: 'Three star, seven year old!'

Mother has quietly moved the bottles out of the way and put them into the press, for she does not care for this display of drink, and now she spreads the huge, gleaming white tablecloth over the other cloth and this adds to the brightness of the place. There is this feeling of things going almost too well, one which Mother always plays down, perhaps feeling that it could get out of hand; she is apprehensive of excited

A party at the Cleggs Arms Hotel in 1927

enthusiasm, and also she may hope, with the bottles out of sight, to hold back the actual drinking until she would have food on the table, but if so my father defeats her in this. He has a bottle out and begins to pour and hand out the drinks – no water added amongst the Irish – and now Uncle gives me a wink to go across and join him for a first taste. The glass is up at my lips, and I do not mind that hot, blinding scurry of the whiskey as it runs down inside me, for I believe whiskey does me good, and I have learnt to toss it back pretty fast. 'I'll bet none of my mates in this street ever tasted whiskey,' I think to myself. 'What a lucky lad am I!'

This Irish drinking on such an occasion is never frivolous or boisterous, but animated by some ancient sense of ceremony, perhaps hinting at memories of greater days and nobler circumstances. And it would seem to me, as young as I am, so different are our Irish ways from those of Lancashire folk, that we each belong to quite separate worlds. We Irish are never without some word about God, the Holy Ghost and the Blessed Virgin, and we go whispering prayers and blessing ourselves a dozen times a day, often furtively – although all this does not preclude outbursts of temper and oaths: possibly allows for them – whilst those decent English people go along without seeming to give Him a thought, except perhaps on Sundays when they avoid whistling. Yet they appear to lead more ordered and proper lives than any of us, and, whilst we take on some show of being Catholic, it is clear that their way of life is more estimable, the conscientious manner they go about their work, their absolute reliability and the uncomplaining manner, and above all, their marked sobriety and eschewing of violence.

Amongst us Irish, I often heard it said that we could learn a lesson in respectable living from them. Death too, which constantly comes into our talk – one speaks of the dead as though in some way they are still alive – is hardly mentioned by the good folk in our street. They, alas, appear to have forgotten the right way of behaviour at a funeral, and are uneasy and uncertain over expressing grief, although a most feeling people. Sleep was a sacred phenomenon to the Irish, one interrupted only in an emergency, but in Lancashire a woman would waken up her husband as he dozed in the rocking-chair after his day's work and ask him had he a penny for two ha'pennies for the gas meter, or one of the children might waken him and ask him was the clock right or was it fast, and he would supply the penny or the answer without any show of irritation and drop off to sleep again.

from

Spin Off from a Lancashire Loom

CATHARINE T. HERFORD

The daughter of a Unitarian minister, Catharine Herford (b. 1896) wrote two books of reminiscences in later life. This memory of Christmas at Stand Chapel near Whitefield, north of Manchester, takes us back to Edwardian times. The chapel was bombed early in the Second World War but Stand Unitarian Church, built in a classical New England style, replaced it in 1955.

Stand Chapel was alone among the Dissenters of the district in having a service on Christmas Day; now it is less uncommon, but the preparations are perhaps different. Christmas Eve at the parsonage meant for us children learning to make puff pastry and literally dozens of mince pies. We had only six oval patty pans – the correct shape, Mother maintained, since the pies represented the manger to which the spices and incense of the Nativity were brought; but trays of round ones had to be allowed, because the evening would be devoted to the Decorators' Supper.

This institution had grown up in the years before I was old

enough to notice, and even so it remained to us parsonage children simply glorious 'noises off'. Decorating the chapel was done after work by invitation; it included supper afterwards, and was strictly limited to 'courting couples'. The lists were made out in the weeks before, and the conversation at meal times turned largely then on who were definite, and whether it would be impolitic to include the so-and-soes, who had perhaps not really achieved more than casual 'walking out' status. For many, the Decorators' Supper was a virtual putting up of the banns! The last of these festive occasions to be remembered in the old parsonage somehow or other had 36 glad souls seated and being regaled.

At 10 p.m. those who were singers formed up as a carol party, setting off on their way along the crest of the hill while the rest helped to clear up. Towards midnight, as my parents rolled into bed, the garden gate would open softly and from the lawn below their window floated up the dear, familiar though possibly unpalatable injunction: 'Christians, awake'. But then, it had been composed on our side of Manchester, so how could it have been otherwise? Or could it?

Earlier on one such evening there arrived a party of small boys, singing quite well, but not the type of verse encouraged in our orthodox society. On being asked where they came from, one little enthusiast volunteered: 'Stand Unitarians'. 'What?' said my mother. 'Come into the light and let me see you.' Not recognising one of them, she realised that the words meant nothing to them and asked quite simply: 'Which Sunday school do you belong to?' She received an equally simple and innocent reply. 'Whatever made you say Stand Unitarians, then?' she questioned. 'Oh,' replied the spokesman. 'They told us to say that, as we should get more money if we did.' She fed them with mince pies, and went back to the rest of the party marvelling at the devious ways of men, the inscrutability of Providence and the value of a reputation to be maintained.

Owd Abrum

DENNIS BALL

Christmas ghosts are not too thick on the ground in Lancashire – little more than a skeleton staff of them, you could say. But Dennis Ball came up with this chilling little bunch in his Lancashire Pastimes *of 1987, with the result that I cannot pass through Walton-le-Dale today without keeping half an eye open for the kind of procession you never saw at Whit Week. It was only after reading his book that I recalled one dark early morning back in the 1970s, when I was driving home to Preston after my night shift with a Manchester newspaper. I had travelled for miles without seeing a living soul, but in Walton-le-Dale I was astonished to find throngs of people making the streets seem as busy as day. At the time I simply took them to be factory workers cursed with hours even more unsociable than mine. And I still* hope *that's what they were . . .*

One of the clergymen at St Leonard's Church, Walton-le-Dale, near Preston, was thought to be dealing with the devil. As the years went by he was left with only one real friend, Owd Abrum, an eccentric who studied herb and plant life and astronomy. As their friendship grew, the minister told Abraham of an experiment he had been wanting to try for

Bringing in the Christmas holly

many years. This would take the form of blending certain herbs and flowers together, at the same time chanting obscure Latin prayers. If this was done on Christmas Eve in the porch of the church, and if the experiment was successful, they would be able to see the faces of all in the parish who would die in the next 12 months.

They waited in the porch together the following Christmas Eve with bunches of bay leaves, mountain ash and holly, and a

large selection of other herb and plant life. Together they chanted the prayers – and suddenly strange music struck up and they saw a procession coming towards the church porch. The weird line of people was made up of several well-known villagers, a handful of strangers – and leading the procession was the clergyman himself. As soon as he saw this he fell down unconscious, and had to be taken home and put to bed. The story became public knowledge, and he was soon visited by almost everyone in the district, wishing to know whether they had been seen in the procession. The villagers troubled him so much that in the end he was forced to leave the area. And some months later, sure enough, news reached Walton-le-Dale that he had died of the plague. What became of Old Abrum is not known; but it seems a safe bet that he did not try the experiment again.

from

Mist Over Pendle

ROBERT NEILL

Published in 1951, Robert Neill's classic novel based on the Lancashire witch legends of the early seventeenth century remains as avidly read as ever. It tells the story of an orphaned girl of Cambridge academic stock who moves

to *live with relatives on the Lancashire and Yorkshire
border and becomes fired with the quest to solve the mystery
of a string of untimely deaths. This excerpt finds Margery
in a more cheerful mood, entering the spirit of a rough
rural party on Christmas Eve and taking her chances with
the Lord of Misrule. The old Christmas custom of the fool
reigning for the evening stems from the bawdy Roman
mid-winter feast of Saturnalia, when masters and slaves
exchanged places for several days. Its influence survives in
a very diluted form in the British Army, when the officers
serve the men's lunch on Christmas Day; the prefects did
the same at the North Manchester grammar school I
attended, but I doubt whether any visiting Roman would
have recognized the scene in Mrs Ludlam's canteen as
Saturnalia!*

Then came supper, crowded, generous and informal. Margery,
in the middle of an excited group, found herself trying to keep
up the talk while she dealt hungrily with a great basin of what
looked like yellow cream and was, she learned, the traditional
frumenty – wheat, boiled in milk and flavoured with cinnamon and sugar. With it was a queer oatmeal bread which she
had not seen before; they told her it was called jannock, and
that the proper thing to do was to dip it in the frumenty and
then eat it while it dripped. Then came what they called mince
pies, shaped like a manger to tell them of a Birth, and stuffed
with every kind of spice to tell them of Gifts that had come
from the East. There was cold goose with wheaten bread; and
nuts and sugar and plums; and mug after mug of the prime
October to help it down. Then, when all was done and the
hungriest stuffed to repletion, the clatter died and the talk
sank to whispers; and without any order given, the company
moved from the centre of the room and pressed themselves
against the dark panels of the walls. Then a trumpet blared

and drums banged noisily; the doors were flung wide, and into the room, tumbling in joyous somersaults, his motley a wild flurry of blue and yellow, came the man who meant Christmas – the crazy Lord of Misrule.

He had a thunderous welcome, and pretended to be angered by it. He belaboured the nearest with his sceptre – an inflated bladder, swinging by a cord from a two-foot stick – and he roared lustily for silence. Since they were so insolent, he told them, they should do penance in proper form. He stalked fiercely round the room, pulling his painted face into grotesque frowns, and Margery, sitting cross-legged on the floor in the front of the throng, suddenly hiccoughed with excitement and amusement. She was promptly punished with the bladder, a great thundering slap that knocked her off her balance and sent her sprawling against her red-haired yeoman, while the room rocked in a gale of laughter. Again the Lord of Misrule waved his bladder for silence, and slowly the laughter died until he could be heard again. They should, he said, do penance by paying homage to his horse – a marvellous proper horse, he said, who was named Old Ball; and whatever more the Lord of Misrule may have meant to say was lost for ever in the stamping and cheering that greeted this.

Again the doors were set wide; again the Lord of Misrule plied his bladder for silence; again the hush throbbed with expectancy. Then, cavorting through the doorway, neighing, kicking and jumping clear from the floor, came the monstrous image of a horse. The stamping and cheering rose to madness, with shrieks and whistles and bangings of mugs. Margery took one look at Old Ball and then swayed helplessly against her neighbour, hurting her ribs with laughter. Old Ball was a huge horse's head, crazily done in wood and canvas; the round bottoms of wine-bottles formed his eyes, and his teeth were painted wooden pegs; below, two stout sticks took the weight and pretended to be his front legs; a great sheet of canvas made

Christmas Eve in the country

his body, and concealed the man who was his hind legs and who worked his tail and jaws. For both moved; there was a great tail of red-bound rope, which flapped wildly; and there was a lower jaw which moved creakingly up and down; and from out of this fantastic mouth there stuck a great iron ladle, gaily hung with ribbons.

The Lord of Misrule swung his bladder, and Old Ball came prancing obediently; and at a shouted command he went romping round the circle, rearing on his hind legs and whinneying noisily, while the applause came in deafening waves. Then, as the laughter began to die, Old Ball went snorting at a stout and bearded yeoman; the jaw moved with a creak, and the yeoman's arm was seized by the painted teeth. He led the laughter himself, while he felt in his pouch; from it he produced two pennies, which he flung into the beribboned ladle. Old Ball promptly released him, and the ladle was suddenly withdrawn between the painted jaws; from somewhere within the beast there was a metallic clang as the pennies dropped, and then the ladle shot out again as Old Ball went snorting after his next victim. This was a portly gentleman in murrey velvet, who jovially produced a silver shilling; another yeoman paid his twopence; Roger was the next, and flung a whole crown into the ladle; a yeoman's wife and somebody's fair-haired daughter gave a penny each; the wife of an Esquire produced a florin; and Old Ball continued inexorably around the circle. But the crowd was growing restless, and began to stir. Someone flung a coin; another followed, and another; and soon coins were being flung at the ladle from all sides, and the Lord of Misrule was jumping wildly after those that fell. Then the climax came. The musicians who had played for the dancing suddenly struck up again, and Old Ball went stamping round the room to the thump of a marching tune. The staid and portly moved hurriedly aside, and the rest rushed wildly at the tail of red-wrapped rope; as many as could get a grip hung fiercely to it and the rest hung as fiercely to them; and soon three-quarters of the company were solemnly tramping a circle in tow of that crazy horse. Then the music came faster – and faster – and faster still. The solemn tramp became a jogging trot; the trot became an unsteady run; and soon there was a wild and whirling romp, till the man in the canvas horse stumbled and fell headlong. His followers sprawled on top of him, and their followers fell across them in a wild hooting chaos while the music ended abruptly in a screech of discord.

Margery was gasping for breath. Her head was in someone's back, and a laughing nut-brown girl was sprawling across her legs. At her side, the red-haired yeoman, one arm still round Margery, was disentangling himself from a plump girl in green. Across the room, Anne Heber, who had gone into it with the best of them, was being hauled to her feet by Roger.

Everywhere fathers were grinning and blowing, while mothers looked anxiously at sons and reprovingly at daughters. And girls who had not yet extricated themselves were being given swift reminders that the mistletoe still hung in the greenery above.

Frumenty and Figgy Pudding

ANNE HIGGINS

The Christmas revellers in Robert Neill's *Mist Over Pendle* were treated to a supper that started with frumenty, an old North Country recipe described in the book as 'wheat, boiled in milk and flavoured with cinnamon and sugar'. The traditional farmhouse way of preparing this dish, much eaten by, though not necessarily beloved of, the Romans who drew the short straw and were despatched to our Northern moors, was to soak a pint of crushed wheat with a pint each of milk and water in a stone jar overnight, and then to bake for three hours in the slowest oven, adding sugar, cinnamon, nutmeg, honey or dried fruit to taste. It was ready when its texture was thick and jelly-like.

If you are low on crushed wheat and stone jars, you could simmer a pint of coarse flour in milk for three hours and then

add two more pints of milk, four ounces of sugar, a dash of cinnamon and a good handful of currants or raisins. Bring this mixture to the boil for another 15 minutes, and you will find its flavour will be by no means impaired if you add a couple of egg yolks and a splash of brandy before serving as a starter.

Figgy pudding – the dish demanded by the carollers in *We Wish You a Merry Christmas* – is another Northern favourite, one that really sticks to your ribs. You need four ounces of stale bread; three ounces of shredded suet; six ounces of figs; a cup of milk; nutmeg; four ounces of flour; salt; a teaspoon of baking powder; and two tablespoons of syrup.

Soak the bread in the milk, chop the figs and mix all the dry ingredients together. Squeeze the bread, mash it with a fork and mix it well with the rest of the ingredients. Put the mixture in a greased basin, cover with a cloth and boil for at least two hours. One for the slimmers, this!

The oddest Lancashire feast I have encountered was the one described by Ben Brierley, the great Victorian dialect writer from Failsworth, in his story *Shoiny Jim's Kesmas Dinner*. Jim told the guests it was to be *Soup au Oldham*, *Turkey au Stretford* and *Poo-ah-Zong de Yarmouth*, but that turned out to be the oatmeal dish the Scots call brose, black pudding and bloaters. From the way Brierley's characters are talking it is obvious that brose – 'browis' or 'breawis' in Lancashire dialect and a first cousin of frumenty – was a usual accompaniment to black pudding. As Brierley's *alter ego* Ab-o'th'-Yate remarks: 'Well, ther's wurr stuff etten nur black puddin's an' breawis, but it's hardly what one expects at a Kesmas dinner.'

Christmas Day for Dolly

One of the world's most rousing and evocative Christmas hymns, *Christians Awake*, was written in a now demolished house in Manchester in 1749. Or at least, a rather rambling verse of rhyming couplets was produced that year by John Byrom and dedicated to his daughter Dorothy with the words 'Christmas Day for Dolly', and an inspirational tune and some prudent editing by hymnal compilers have done the rest.

The fine work of those rewrite men can be appreciated when you consider some of the lines they pruned. Imagine, for instance, throwing back your head and singing:

> *Joseph and Mary, a distressed Pair,*
> *Guard the sole object of th' Almighty's Care;*
> *To human eyes none present but they two,*
> *Where Heav'n was pointing its concentred view!*

Byrom was born at Kersal Cell on the Manchester outskirts in 1692, and some romantics have supposed that he composed the verse in this atmospheric old mansion. In fact it was almost certainly written at his town house in Hanging Ditch, at the corner of Hunter's Lane, one of a half-timbered row demolished in 1821.

He was a scholar, the creator of a shorthand system, a high churchman with Jacobite leanings and an interest in religious

A contemporary drawing of John Byrom, a tall and latterly
stooped figure

debate, and a poet capable of lines as glorious as 'Rise to adore
the mystery of love' and as patchy as those seen above. He was
a fellow of Trinity College, Cambridge, but his doctorate – he
was forever Dr Byrom in Manchester – was a figment of the
imagination, for while he went to France allegedly to study

· A Lancashire Christmas ·

John Byrom's house in Hanging Ditch, Manchester,
demolished in 1821

medicine, he did not take a degree. Conspiracy theorists prefer
to think he was there for Jacobite purposes. All in all, his was
an odd, off-beat life, and even after his death in 1763 there was
a final bizarre twist when his estate was fined £5 because he
was not buried in woollen, as a somewhat macabre law
designed to boost the textile trade then demanded. Since he
was reputed to be one of the tallest men in England, a
towering, gangling figure, perhaps they had simply been
unable to find a piece long enough.

It is thus very much to *Christians Awake* that he owes his
immortality – and for that he must pay a great debt of
gratitude to the tune's composer, John Wainwright. A Stockport man, he graduated from being organist of his home
town's parish church to the Collegiate Church in Manchester,
now the cathedral. He was a friend of Byrom, and set his
words to music some time in 1750. The writer's diary entry for
Christmas Day that year reads: 'The singing men and boys
with Mr Wainwright came here and sang *Christians Awake.*'
'Here', of course, would have been Hanging Ditch, just round
the corner from the cathedral.

The manuscript of the original poem – most probably a
rough draft, rather than the fair copy presented to Dolly – is

The original manuscript of 'Christians Awake' now in
Chetham's Library in Manchester

now kept at Chetham's Library, the priceless Manchester-based collection. By strange coincidence, Byrom applied for the post of librarian at Chetham's after he returned from France, but was turned down. The tattered and folded paper was discovered entirely by chance by the head of Manchester public libraries at the auction of a major private library in the mid-1880s. He recognized it for what it was, slipped it back into the book in which he had found it, and bought it and several others in the lot for next to nothing. His good fortune became Chetham's when he presented the library with the poem.

There remains a deal of muddle about John Byrom in Manchester. Some people will swear that he was born in the Wellington Inn, and he is often confused with the Lord whom

Lady Caroline Lamb found mad, bad and dangerous to know. Even the tune to his hymn has borne a bewildering number of names over the years, skipping like some Beeching-axed branch line from *Yorkshire* to *Ashton*, *Mottram* and *Huddersfield* before settling aptly on *Stockport*. It is cheering to those of us who lead chaotic lives that out of this cacophony can have emerged a work of such pure and lucid genius; but I would still like to know what Dolly, then aged about twenty, *really* thought of daddy's Christmas present on 25 December, 1749.

Breakfast at Windsor

EMILY GLENCROSS

Subtitled 'Memories of a Salford Childhood, 1914–1928', Emily Glencross's book speaks eloquently of life in what was perhaps the ultimate slum city of England. She started to write at the age of sixty-five, but her memories of her early days, sometimes aided and abetted by newspaper clippings, are still crystal-clear. The Windsor of the book's title was the Windsor Institute Ragged School, one of those brave little backstreet missions that was in the

· A Lancashire Christmas ·

*business of saving young souls, but just as often found itself
preserving young lives. Mrs Glencross has fond memories of
the annual Christmas breakfast at the institute, 'for many
children their Christmas, full stop'. But in the year she
turned seven there was an even bigger treat in store.*

Christmas at home was an effort for our parents. A week or so
beforehand, if Dad was not drinking all his money away, they
would put on their best clothes one Saturday afternoon and
take the tram to town, where they would buy each of us a little
something from Woolworth's. On Christmas morning we
would all be up long before we went to the Christmas breakfast
and would each go to our special place. Mine became one side
of the sewing machine that stood under the kitchen window
overlooking the street. There was always a small toy of some
kind, an apple and an orange, a handful of nuts and a brand
new penny. By the time we had been to Windsor Institute and
received a bag of goodies – and each year we were given really
nice presents – Christmas was complete. I was around eight or
nine years old when I was given a doll, truly the best present I
had ever had in my life.

Windsor Institute was well known for many good works
throughout my childhood, and one in particular from which I
benefited was at the Christmas I became seven years of age,
1921. My sister Mary was 11 years old, and was one of the girls
chosen at Sunday school to spend a week at a holiday home in
Rowarth. She was allowed to take me, as I was her younger
sister. We were there for Christmas, and I can remember it well.
After a train journey to Marple, we walked with the teachers into
Rowarth, where we were met by the staff of the home. I remember
the dormitory of little beds, and having one to myself, which was
marvellous; we were sleeping four in a bed at home.

We came downstairs each morning and washed ourselves
outside the house – I remember it was so cold! There was a row

A festive mill scene in 1935

of small enamel bowls in a kind of lean-to shed. The dining room was lovely, with a huge fireplace burning logs, and in the corner was a Christmas tree which really made our eyes shine. On Christmas morning we were taken to church in the village, and I well remember walking through the snow across the fields. It was sheer paradise to all the girls, big and small, from the streets of Salford, to see the beautiful countryside with horses in the fields and to hear the mooing of cows as we passed the farms. We came back to have dinner, and each of us received a small gift from the Christmas tree. After dinner we were invited to sit around that lovely fire, we smaller ones sitting on the huge rug, and the older girls on chairs. We were listening to the matron of the home, who was reading us a story, when the bell rang out at the front door; we could hear voices, one of them familiar.

It was that of Mr J.P. McDougall, the Sunday school superintendent, who had come out specially on Christmas Day to see us enjoying ourselves. We all gave him a cheer, and our Christmas greetings. I remember his face so well, his smile partially hidden by the short beard he wore and his eyes sparkling as he looked around him. I am sure our faces were indeed a picture. On the wall of the dining room above the table was a picture of Jesus standing at a doorway with a lamp in His hand, *I am the way, the truth and the life*. Mr McDougall spoke to us for around half an hour about that picture. You could have heard a pin drop, it was so quiet, and the memory has stayed with me always, for that was the kind of man he was. He was the way, the truth and the life to us. That morning he would have been at the Christmas breakfast at the ragged school, then no doubt spent some time with his own family, and then on to Rowarth in appalling weather to see us. He was given another rousing cheer when he left.

I remember going out for walks around the lovely country-side, and even over the fields into New Mills. For both my sister Mary and me that was our first time away from home at Christmas, and it was to be another three or four years before my next holiday. That was to Squires Gate Holiday Camp — again with the Windsor Institute.

Eaur Sarah's Chap: His Christmas Day At Th' Girl's

TEDDY ASHTON

In real life Teddy Ashton was C. Allen Clarke, a Blackpool-based writer and publisher who was a mainstay of the Lancashire dialect movement from late Victorian times well into the inter-war years. Clarke was a staunch socialist and no stranger to serious political debate, but he let his hair down through his dialect-speaking pseudo-nym's Teddy Ashton's Journal (A Gradely Paper For Gradely Folk), *which was 'at rest' by 1908, and through the far longer-lasting* Teddy Ashton's Annual, *a Christmas offering first launched in 1892.*

Perhaps the most entertaining of the long-running Eaur Sarah's Chap *series, this extract comes from the* Annual *of 1922. The dialect is not hard to read; and in its portrayal of that confusing stage in a young man's life when loyalties are divided between parents and lover, it works more touchingly and truthfully than the writings of many a more accomplished hand. Besides, a writer cannot be all wrong when he can come up with a phrase like 'Dan had nowt to say' to encapsulate the silence after a young*

man has been subjected to a justifiable tirade from his mum
— or the bemused maternal question 'Is it courtin' theaur't
doin', or has ta jeined a war?'

On th' Christmas Eve, as Dan an' his girl were walkin' deawn
Lovers' Lane under th' frosty stars, Sarah said, rayther shyly,
'My mother's expectin' thee to have dinner wi' us to-morn.'

'Who'll be theer?' said Dan.

'Aw th' lot of us — wed brothers an' sisters an' their
families,' said Sarah. 'We allus have a family gatherin' on
Christmas Day. Theau'll come, weren't ta?'

'Ay, I'll meet thee to-morn mornin' somewheer,' said Dan.

Teddy Ashton's Annual in 1908 and 1909

'We could go to th' chapel fust, an' then fro' theer to eaur heause,' said Sarah.

'Very weel,' said Dan.

It were midneet when he left Sarah, after havin' a bit o' supper wi' her an' her mother an' feyther, for folks seldom gets to bed early on Christmas Eve. Sarah's mother were busy seein' that everythin' were ready for th' annual feast an' family gatherin': th' turkey, puddin' an' aw th' rest o't. Th' pictures an' clock were decorated wi' holly an' evergreens, an' there were a tiny bit o' mistletoe fastened to th' gaspipe that hung fro' th' middle o' th' ceilin'. Sarah's mother, Mrs Grundy, copt Dan under this an' gan him a kiss that made th's furniture shake.

'Theer, Sarah, I've kailed thee,' hoo said, an' Dan an' Sarah had a big blush together.

When Dan kissed Sarah good-neet on th' doorstep th' church bells were ringin', and reaund th' corner they could yer some carol-singers sweetly renderin' *While Shepherds Watched Their Flocks* an' then *Christians Awake* an' Dan felt heaw wonderful an' glorious th' Christmas hymns seaunded i' th' peaceful neet.

'A merry Christmas, Dan,' said Sarah, suddenly kissin' him; an' Dan, as he returned th' happy wish in another kiss, were sure he were on th' very doorstep o' Paradise.

As he walked whum through th' dark, quiet streets full o' th' strange blessed influence o' Christmas, yerrin' neaw an' then carol-singers i' th' distance, Dan felt thrilled by mooar than he could utter. What a beautiful an' blissful combination were Christmas an' courtin'!

Next mornin', which were Christmas Day, Dan were rayther late to breakfast, an', lookin' at th' clock, seed that he'd have to horry to meet Sarah at ten, as they'd arranged.

'Theau't in a sweat o'er thy breakfast,' said his mother, Mrs Bickett; 'it corn't do thee much good gobblin' it at that rate. Tak' thy time.'

'I'm gooin' to chapel,' said Dan; 'an' I'st ha' to be sharp, or I'st be late.'

Dan knowed that tellin' his mother he were gooin' t' chapel would please her.

'It seams that a girl con get a lad to do mooar than ever his mother con,' said Mrs Bickett. 'What time will ta be whum to thy dinner?'

'Eh – eh?' flustered Dan.

'I axed thee what time theau'd be whum to thy dinner,' said his mother.

'Er – I durn't think I'm comin' whum to my dinner,' said Dan.

'Wha'?' said his mother. 'Not comin' whum to thy dinner, an' Christmas Day, too?'

'Er – I've been invited eaut,' said Dan.

'An' jumped at th' chance,' said Mrs Bickett. 'Anywheer afore awhum.'

Dan put on his best lapcooat an' his hat.

'I suppose tha'll be whum to thy tay, then?' said his mother.

'I – durn't think so,' said Dan. 'I've been invited eaut to tay, too.'

'Oh,' said Mrs Bickett, 'hadn't ta better tak' thy bed too, an' then theau con stop aw together? So I reckon we'st see no mooar on thee till midneet?'

Dan had nowt to say.

'An' me geet such a nice turkey,' said his mother, 'an' such a nice puddin'; an' eawr Bob an' his wife an' thy uncle Bill an' his wife comin' to their tay wi' us – what shall I tell 'em when they ax wheer theau art?'

Dan had still nowt to say. He put his hat on, an' went tort th' door.

'Good mornin', mother,' he said.

'Good mornin',' said Mrs Bickett. 'See as theau comes whum undamaged.'

Underwear and Utensils for making Dainty Cakes and
Puddings as Christmas gifts: advertisements from *Teddy
Ashton's Annual* in Edwardian times

93

His mother looked a bit sad. It were th' fust time Dan had ever missed havin' his Christmas dinner awhum. Dan felt her feelin's, and had a thowt to ax her if he should bring Sarah to tay – that would be fair, he thowt – him to ha' dinner at Sarah's, an' her to go to tay wi' him to his folks – but he couldn't muster pluck to mak' th' proposition. He didn't know heaw his mother would tak' it. (Why, hoo'd ha' jumped at it, if he'd nobbut known).

So Dan went eaut, while his mother bent o'er th' big pon in which th' Christmas puddin' were beilin', an' maybe it were nobbut a bit o' sweat or steam – for surely it could never be a tear tricklin' deawn her face.

'Well, well,' hoo said, 'I suppose everythin' has to have a beginnin'; even one's childer leeavin' th' nest; it's th' way o' th' world, but aw th' same – this beginnin' that meeans endin' o' summat else is rayther –'

An' hoo stared intently at th' Christmas puddin'. Meanwhile, Dan met Sarah, an' they went to chapel together, an' then to Sarah's whum, wheer there were awready a fair muster o' th' family tribe, including a babby an' hauve-a-dozen childer, fro' aw parts o' th' compass.

Dan, bein' awmost th' same as one o' th' family neaw, felt mooar awhoam amung his sweetheart's folks an' kin, an' had even getten used to th' owdest sister's chaffin' husband – his name were Ted Bunter, whilst his wife were cawd Mary Jane – an' to owd Grundy, an' everybody else, an' t' way they had, except, happen, Sarah's two younger mischievous brothers, Ben and Bill; but these two were better behaved than usual this time, happen because it were Christmas Day, or happen because Dan had gan 'em tuppence apiece; anyhow, they played no wuss trick on him than teein' his cooat-laps to th' knife-box on th' little table i' th' scullery when Dan went to wash his honds after dinner, layin' his cooat on th' table again th' knife-box while he did so, an' when he'd washed hissel, an' geet howd of his cooat to put it on, he jerked th' knife-box off th' table wi' a flutter, an' a lot o' spoons went to th' floor wi' such a rattlin' din that Mrs Grundy coom rushin' into th' scullery to see whatever were up, an' swore to breik them two young imps' backs — they'd discreetly vanished — as soon as ever hoo could lay honds on 'em.

Th' stitches o' one o' Dan's laps were ripped a bit by th' weight o' th' box, but Sarah said hoo could soon put that reet wi' a needle an' thread.

There's no need to tell yo' th' tale o' th' dinner; heaw they aw whacked into th' turkey an' pratoes an' puddin'; they stuffed theirsels till they were too sleepy to stir, an' lolled abeaut th' cheers an' sofa aw afternoon, except Dan an' Sarah, what went for a walk, an' Ted Bunter, what went to th' footbaw match.

'Kock-y-kaily-krow!': Dan and Ted Bunter get down to some serious cock-feightin'

After tay they had singin' and games, come-an'-sit-on-my-knee an' musical cheers an' sich-like sport, an' Dan thout that if heaven weren't rayther like Christmas, it wouldn't be up to much.

Then Ted Bunter said 'Let's ha' some cock-feightin',' an' Dan wondered what were comin' neaw.

'Come on, Dan,' said Ted, 'thee an' me'll have a do, just to set th' baw rowlin'.'

'Durn't,' whispered Sarah to Dan – they were sit together on th' sofa – 'it's too rough a game.'

'Here, what's Sarah sayin'?' said Ted. 'Is hoo freetent on thee gettin' kilt, Dan? Ne'er mind her. An' if he does get kilt, he's not th' only mon i' th' world, is he?'

'He's th' only mon I want, so's heaw,' said Sarah, beaut stoppin' to think, an' there were loud lowfin', while Ted said, banteringly, 'Theau didn't allus talk like that. What abeaut that mon wi' th' red nut as theau used to run after?'

Sarah flushed angrily, an' said: 'I never used to run after nobody, an' it's a good job that everybody knows thee an' taks no notice o' what theau says, Ted Bunter.'

'Dear me!' said Ted, in mock tragedy, 'we're gettin' eaur paddy up. We murn't be spokken to neaw, as we'n geet a chap an' had him to his dinner on Christmas Day. Heawever, come on, Dan, an' let's have a cock-feight, an' after that we'll have a dust at Are You There? Come on, it wern't hurt thee.'

'What done we do?' axed Dan.

'Sithee, I'll show thee,' said Ted. 'Squat deawn on th' rug like this, spikin' thysel' together by howdin' a walkin' stick behind thy legs, i' th' knee-jeints, an' grippin' it wi' thy honds. Two of us faces one another, an' tries to shove one another o'er wi' eaur feet. Him as rowls o'er th' fust has lost. Come on – just for three tries. Him as gets two eaut o' three is th' winner. It's lovely exercise, mon; it's a grand preparation for matrimony.'

Though Sarah towd him not to, Dan were inclined to have a bout at cock-feightin' wi' Ted.

In fact, though he were pleased as nobbut a silly lover con be wi' th' thout that Sarah didn't want him to get hurt or shoved abeaut off his dignity, he also thout (as likewise nobody but a silly lover does) that he'd show he were heroic an' freetent o' nowt, an' thus gain mooar glory in her een.

So, despite Sarah's pratty entreaties, Dan had a cock-feight wi' Ted.

As him an' Ted ceaurt ready, facin' one another, wi' their toes together, an' t' others aw merrily lookin' on, Ted said: 'Theau owt to do weel at this job, Dan, theau's a tidy foot, owd mon.'

'It's noan hauve as big as thine,' said Sarah indignantly to Ted.

'Watch me scatter th' foe,' said Ted, an' he begun pushin' at Dan's shoon wi' his toes, while Dan were tryin' hard to get his toes under Ted's soles, an' thus upset him.

Nobody who's never tried cock-feightin' has any idea what hard wark it is; sweat were soon rowlin' deawn th' faces o' Dan an' Ted.

Then aw at once Dan went sprawlin' o'er, reet again Sarah's legs, while Ted cried 'Kock-y-kaily-krow!'

Dan tried hard i' th' second reaund, but he couldn't o'erthrow Ted, what sent him comically rowlin' o'er again. 'Two to me,' said Ted, 'Kock-y-kaily-krow!' An' th' spectators roared at th' sport.

I' th' third reaund Dan put forth his utmost, but in vain. Ted upset him wi' such force that Dan went flyin' on his back among th' fireirons, an' cut th' reet side of his forehead.

'Oh, it's bleedin',' cried Sarah.

'Howd thy husht!' said Ted. 'He's noan kilt! A bit o' plester will put him aw reet.'

'I'd be ashamed o' mysel' if I were thee,' said Sarah, 'to maul an innocent lad so.'

'Oh, it's nobbut a scrat,' said Dan, gooin' into th' scullery to wash his face. Sarah followed him wi' some skin-plester, an' it felt so nice havin' her fingers on his face that Dan wooshed he had a million mooar little cuts on him; an' he put his arm reaund her an' squeezed her while hoo doctored him.

They were such a while that at last Ted sheauted 'What's yo' two doin' i' th' scullery? Are ta kissin' him better, Sarah?' At this everybody roared, an' Dan an' Sarah coom eawt blooshin' together.

Then Ted said he were sorry he'd hurt Dan; it were quite an accident; an' Dan said he knowed it were, an' it were nowt to bother abeaut.

They went on wi' their frolic an' fun, an' had such a jolly neet that th' heaurs were gone in no time, an' Dan, when he parted fro' Sarah on th' doorstep, were wooshin' that there were a Christmas Day at least once a week.

* * *

When Dan geet whum, his mother, aw by hersel', were sit up waitin' for him.

'What's ta been doin' at thy face?' hoo said, as hoo seed th' plester. 'Theau'll be comin' whum kilt next. Theau must get into some bonny company.'

Dan said nowt, but pood his coat off, an' as he turned to lay it on th' dresser his mother copt seet o' th' back of his treausers, which were awmost rubbed away by th' cock-feightin'. 'Well, I never,' hoo said. 'Theau'll be comin' whum wi' thy shirt-lap hangin' eaut behind some day. An'' — as hoo picked his cooat up to look at that — 'thy cooat-lap torn, too. Clooas in an awful`state, an' face cut. What does it mean? Is it courtin' theau't doin', or has ta jeined a war?'

Dan piked off to bed, wheer he lee thinkin' o' Sarah, an' were very happy.

Theear at t' Manger

The retelling of Bible stories is a frequent theme of Lancashire dialect verse, and it is hardly surprising that the Nativity should have inspired many a fine poem. I have chosen three, finding them all sincere and moving, but must confess my special admiration for Quiet in Bethlehem, *written several years ago by John Sparth of Accrington. I cannot believe he could have produced it without knowing and loving T.S. Eliot's* Journey of the Magi, *the one that begins 'A cold coming we had of it . . . ' That having been said, his poem is rich in strikingly original images, and he speaks with a voice that is entirely his own.*

Quiet in Bethlehem

Ask owd Jake theear. It's likely e'll mind on
O' a thing like thad. Heigh, Jacob! Wakken up.
Theear's somebody heear as wants ta ask thee summat . . .
T' poor owd mon's gettin' deeaf – it's age, yo' knaw.
(And Jacob stirred from drowsing, slowly and thickly
As oil in a jar).

'Do Ah remember a star?
Whad star? Oh, thad! Ay, proper breet it were,
A bobby-dazzler. Seemed to come an' stand
Reight ower wheear th' inn's owd stables were . . .
They'n been pood deawn. Improvements. T' other lan'lord.
Ay, theear's allus progress somewheear.

'Did Ah know
Whad thad star meant? Oo did? We guessed, o' coorse.
Specially when them bigwigs wi' theear camels,
Waitin'-men, an' falderols, tha knaws.
Some gov'ment do; investigation-like.
Some said a rooad bein' built fro' Jerusalem
To reych aw t' warld. An' suchlike gawmless talk.
Then aw them shepherds flockin' deawn fro' th' ills.
An' t'weren't no shearin' time, nor market then.

'Ah put id deawn to fooak jus' gettin' restless;
Gallivantin', rich an' poor alike,
Lookin' for summat fresh, a proper change.
Though why pick Bedlih'm? It's quiet 'ere.
But 'appen t' shepherds, feelin' short o' women
– Tha knaws heaw t'is . . . An' wi' thad taxin' lark
An' lots o' men abeawt, id were a time
For women on t' loose.

'That's t' other sooart;
But oo were a daycent body, nobbut young
An' this 'er fost. Ay, 'appen th' only one.
Yet wheear oo fits i' aw this moitherin'
Wi' stars an' shepherds, bigwigs – an' Ah 'eeard
Some talk of angels – God aboon knaws whad!
Yo'll think Ah'm daft. But me, Ah did mi job;
Went in an' wattered t' beeasts, an' bed 'em deawn.

'Id were a bonny lad.
Ah've wondered sometimes
Whad coom on 'im. 'Is fooak, tha knaws, were 'eear
For t' census. Just to mek their cross.
Ah've wondered. Seemed a daycent, quiet pair,
Nowt special. Yet Ah still remember 'em.

That's quare! Not brazenin' theirsel's abroad
Like these two preychers wi' their "Son o' Man"
An' "One mun dee for t' people". Rantin' on
Like they'd walked 'and-i'-glove wi' God Hissel',
Or seen Messiah swaddled like yon child.
Ah meks nowt on id!

'Lead a quiet life
Beawt aw this mad excitement. Do thy nook
An' if nod creawned, tha'll nod be crucified!
It's dry wark talkin'. Ay, Ah'll hev a sup.
  . . . Nay, Bedlih'm's allus bin a quiet place.'

John Sparth

Tha' Wur Theer?

Tha' wur theer
Dost seh?

Did t' see t' leet?

It wur breet
As day —
Must a' bin
A star.
But it wur far.

Did t' see t' child?

Ay, an' t' mother mild
As milk,
An' Joseph's een
As 'e gazed
Fur mazed.

· A Lancashire Christmas ·

An' wot on t' creawd?

Not sheawtin' leawd.
Just quiet like
An' smilin',
Like any morn
A babby's born.

An' t' shepherds wi' thur sheep?

Ay, 'afe asleep
They'd walked that far
Followin' t' leet.
Frikkened still,
But gazin' thur fill!

An t' wise men, wur they theer?

Stondin' as near
As e'er they could –
Rum gifts they browt.
Nowt fer playin',
Moostly fer prayin'!

An' wot did t' think abeawt it a'?

Weel, Ah wur glad
Fer t' mother's joy
An' t' fayther's pride –
But it wur strange –
Whilst babby slept,
We stood reet quiet,
Smilin' fer love . . .
An' then we wept.

Lucy Austin

102

· A Lancashire Christmas ·

Th' Innkeeper's Wife

Id wor Kesmus Eve, an' December-cowd,
When them two strangers cum;
'We ought to hev fun 'em a bed,' he said.
'They'd betther ha' stayed awhum.'
He knew verra weel as th' inn wor full
An' Ah'd bin on mi feet o' day.
Here, theer, at iveryone's beck an' co'
But *men* never think thad way!

An' as he hurried to fotch mooar wine
He wor muttherin' unther his breath:
'Poor lass! Eh, hoo looks soa tired an' pale,
They'n cum fro' Nazareth.
Ah couldn't think of 'em eawt i' t' dark
Soa Ah showed 'em t' stable dooar.
An' left 'em a loaf an' a lantern, an'
A bundle o' straw fer t' flooar.

'An as Ah cum back Ah looked at t' stars.
By heck! Even t' lil' 'uns blazed!
But over eawr roof, yo should ha' sin!
Ah tell yo, Ah stood amazed!
Thad star — eawr star — it shone as breet
As ever a star could shine!'
'Yo an' yor talk o' stars,' Ah sed,
'Fer pity's sake, fotch yon wine!

'Shift yorsel'! We need wood fer t' fires,
An' hay fer yon merchant's horse;
An' tuthri o' t' camel-men are drunk

· A Lancashire Christmas ·

An' – wod did yo say? Ov course
Ah'll find a drink fer yor *special* guests,
(Vagrants more like, they are),
An' a sup o' broth if we've ony left,
An' yes, Ah'll look at yon star!'

But an heawr ud passed ere Ah'd t' time t' spare –
As Ah hurried eawt wi' a sigh,
Ah fun theer wor others theer afore,
An' Ah yeerd a babby cry!
Id wor *my* torn neaw to ston' amazed,
He led theer i' t' lantern-glow
Wi' th'owd mare an' t' chickens lookin' on,
An t' shepherds kneelin' below.

An' Ah felt fur shamed ov o' t' things Ah'd sed
An' ov t' welcome Ah'd nod given,
Fer one o' t' shepherds whispered to me
As t' babby wor t' King ov Heaven!
A miracle? Nay, Ah still dorn'd know,
But Ah breathed a soft Amen,
Fer Ah knew someheaw there'd nod be a birth
Or a dawn like thad agen.

Joan Pomfret

from

William's Truthful Christmas

RICHMAL CROMPTON

As a child I never saw Just William as a Lancashire lad;
however grubby his knees or crinkled his socks, he seemed to
me to be rooted forever in a Home Counties world of French
windows and afternoon tea. When I grew older the first
blow to my preconceptions about him was the realization
that Richmal Crompton was a woman; the second was the
discovery that the boy upon whom he was modelled was
brought up just a couple of miles from my childhood home.
Richmal Crompton was the daughter of the Revd E.J.S.
Lamburn, a master at Bury Grammar School from 1876
to 1915, and William's character was inspired largely by
her brother John. The family lived a little way south of
the town centre on the Manchester Road.

John was educated at his father's school and Manches-
ter University before going on to such varied pursuits as
police work in Rhodesia, trading in China and the study
of natural history; he even helped out with William plots
when his sister's inspiration flagged. But perhaps the most

fascinating fact of all about him was unearthed by William Amos in his brilliant work of literary detection The Originals (*Jonathan Cape, 1985*). *From him comes the mind-boggling information that both Lamburn and Air Commodore Cecil George Wigglesworth, the role model for Biggles, served together with the RAF in Iceland in the Second World War. 'Biggles and William tucked away in Iceland,' Amos muses. 'Imagine the havoc that pair could have caused had Britain allowed them to be captured . . .'*

This excerpt is from a story in the fifth William book, Still William, *published in 1925; Christmas, with its family responsibilities, was never the young rascal's happiest time of year, but the trouble really began when the vicar urged his flock to 'speak the truth one with another and cast aside deceit and hypocrisy' over the festive season . . .*

William awoke early on Christmas Day. He had hung up his stocking the night before and was pleased to see it fairly full. He took out the presents quickly but not very optimistically. He had been early disillusioned in the matter of grown-ups' capacity for choosing suitable presents. Memories of prayer books and history books and socks and handkerchiefs floated before his mental vision . . . Yes, as bad as ever! . . . a case containing a pen and pencil and ruler, a new brush and comb, a purse (empty) and a new tie . . . a penknife and a box of toffee were the only redeeming features. On the chair by his bedside was a book of Church History from Aunt Emma and a box containing a pair of compasses, a protractor and a set square from Uncle Frederick . . .

William dressed, but as it was too early to go down he sat on the floor and ate all his tin of toffee. Then he turned his attention to his Church History book. He read a few pages but the character and deeds of the saintly Aidan so exasperated him that he was driven to relieve his feelings by taking his new pencil from its case and adorning the saint's picture by the addition of a top hat and spectacles. He completed the alterations by a moustache and by changing the book the saint held into an attaché case. He made similar alterations to every picture in the book . . . St Oswald seemed much improved by them and this cheered William considerably. Then he took his penknife and began to carve his initials upon his brush and comb . . .

William appeared at breakfast wearing his new tie and having brushed his hair with his new brush or rather with what was left of his new brush after his very drastic initial carving. He carried under his arm his presents for his host and hostess. He exchanged 'Happy Christmas' gloomily. His resolve to cast away deceit and hypocrisy and speak the truth one with another lay heavy upon him. He regarded it as an obligation that could not be shirked. William was a boy of great tenacity of purpose. Having once made up his mind to a course he pursued it regardless of consequences . . .

'Well, William, darling,' said his mother. 'Did you find your presents?'

'Yes,' said William gloomily. 'Thank you.'

'Did you like the book and instruments that Uncle and I gave you?' said Aunt Emma brightly.

'No,' said William gloomily and truthfully. 'I'm not int'rested in Church History an' I've got something like those at school. Not that I'd want 'em,' he added hastily, 'if I hadn't 'em.'

'*William*,' screamed Mrs Brown in horror. 'How can you be so ungrateful?'

'I'm not ungrateful,' explained William wearily. 'I'm only bein' truthful. I'm casting aside deceit an' . . . an' hyp-hyp-what he said. I'm only sayin' that I'm not int'rested in Church

History nor in those inst'ments. But thank you very much for 'em.'

There was a gasp of dismay and a horrified silence during which William drew his paper packages from under his arm.

'Here are your Christmas presents from me,' he said.

The atmosphere brightened. They unfastened their parcels with expressions of anticipation and Christian forgiveness upon their faces. William watched them, his face registering only patient suffering.

'It's very kind of you,' said Aunt Emma, still struggling with the string.

'It's not kind,' said William, still treading doggedly the path of truth. 'Mother said I'd got to bring you something.'

Mrs Brown coughed suddenly and loudly but not in time to drown the fatal words of truth . . .

'But still – er – very kind,' said Aunt Emma though with less enthusiasm.

At last she brought out a small pincushion.

'Thank you very much, William,' she said. 'You really oughtn't to have spent your money on me like this.'

'I din't,' said William stonily. 'I hadn't any money, but I'm very glad you like it. It was left over from Mother's stall at the Sale of Work, an' Mother said it was no use keepin' it for nex' year because it had got so faded.'

Again Mrs Brown coughed loudly but too late. Aunt Emma said coldly:

'I see. Yes. Your mother was quite right. But thank you all the same, William.'

Uncle Frederick had now taken the wrappings from his present and held up a leather purse.

'Ah, this is a really useful present,' he said jovially.

'I'm 'fraid it's not very useful,' said William. 'Uncle Jim sent it to Father for his birthday but Father said it was no use 'cause the catch wouldn' catch so he gave it to me to give to you.'

Uncle Frederick tried the catch.

'Um . . . ah . . .' he said. 'Your father was quite right. The catch won't catch. Never mind, I'll send it back to your father as a New Year present . . . what?'

As soon as the Brown family was left alone it turned upon William in a combined attack.

'I *warned* you!' said Ethel to her mother.

'He ought to be hung,' said Robert.

'William, how *could* you?' said Mrs Brown.

'When I'm bad you go on at me,' said William with exasperation, 'an' when I'm tryin' to lead a holier life and cast aside hyp-hyp-what he said, you go on at me. I dunno what I *can* be. I don't mind bein' hung. I'd as soon be hung as keep havin' Christmas over an' over again simply every year the way we do . . .'

Christmas Day in the Workhouse

MOLLIE CARNEY

John and Hannah Wibberley were master and matron of a workhouse in South-east Lancashire, near Ashton-under-Lyne. Their joint salary was £110 a year, plus full residential

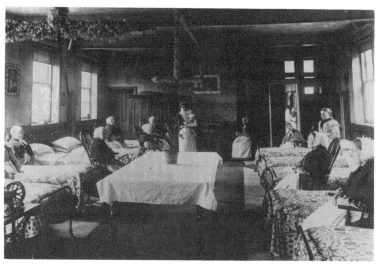

Yes, this is Christmas in the Oldham workhouse at the turn
of the century; you can tell by the decorations around the
overhead pipes

emoluments which included their food, a furnished residence,
a personal maid for Hannah and all the domestic help needed
to run their household.

John Wibberley was a kind, just man who always boasted
that he had never had to resort to asking for police support in
keeping control, as many of his colleagues had from time to
time. He applied all the rules, but as lightly as he could. The
duties of master and matron were laid down in *The Poor Law
Officers' Manual*, the bible of the workhouse.

John allowed the inmates to choose their daily task, as far as
it was possible. They were also able to approach him with their
grievances, and know that he would listen and consider their
case. The inmates respected and liked him, and perhaps this
was his secret of keeping control, for their rights were few.

As matron, Hannah found a full rein for expressing her

passion for an economical way of living. Food was weighed out as prescribed by the local government board dietary tables. Displayed on the walls were the large cardboard charts which covered all the diets possible – infirmary diet for the sick, house diet for the able-bodied. A change could be prescribed only by the medical officer, and food not mentioned on the dietary sheets was not allowed at all, except on Christmas Day or any public festival or thanksgiving.

In 1907 the cost of the 114 inmates on the local ratepayers was 2s. 11d. each a week for provisions, $1\frac{1}{2}$d. per meal per head and 3d. per head a week for clothing. Labour costs were not taken into account, and neither were the fruits of the inmates' toil. Vegetables were grown on the institution land, as was any fruit that survived the Northern climate. Pigs, cows and hens were all tended by inmates. In many ways it was almost a self-supporting community.

The routine of mealtimes did not vary. Inmates assembled in the large glass-roofed dining hall and silently took their places by the long, scrubbed wooden tables. The men in their blue and white cotton jackets and rough cotton trousers stood on one side of the hall, and on the other were the women and children in their blue striped cotton dresses. The master would then walk down the centre of the hall and mount the dais at the end, and when there was absolute silence he would give the signal for grace to be sung. This over, the matron would supervise the handing down of food along the tables. When the meal was over grace would again be sung, and at a given signal from the master the inmates would file quietly out of the dining hall.

One person who recalls life as a workhouse child remembers breakfast of bread and milk, the milk skimmed and the bread never fresh. Dinner time meals varied, sometimes stew or tasteless, watery broth with dumplings in it. Rice puddings, also made from skimmed milk, were the standard sweet. The children did have fresh vegetables, but they were never encouraged to ask for second helpings. Invariably, tea, bread and butter was the last meal of the day. There was no supper, and bedtime was very early.

On Christmas Day the inmates rested from their labours and were given a feast. The day began as usual at 7 a.m. with breakfast in the dining hall, suitably festooned with holly by the workhouse officers. The greenery had been sent down as a gift from the well-stocked gardens of a local cotton magnate, and depending on the generosity of his head gardener and the affability of the workhouse attendants, some of the holly found its way into the drab day rooms where the inmates spent their leisure hours.

Breakfast over, the inmates formed into their religious denominations to attend services. By now all the men were in their Sunday suits of grey striped worsted, and the women in their navy woollen dresses and white mob caps. It was thus that they assembled to hear the institution chaplain invite them to thank God from whom all blessings flowed.

Next in the Christmas Day ritual came the visit of the chairman of the board of governors, members of the committee and the mayor. Touring the institution, these visitors would speak to selected inmates, exchanging seasonal greetings and shaking hands with those whose age commanded some show of respect.

At noon the inmates would file into the dining hall, where the members of the board of guardians and the master and matron were assembled to watch the paupers enjoy their treat of roast beef and pork, vegetables, puddings and pies. Each man was issued with a Christmas pint of beer, and the women had a choice of cordials.

Apples, oranges, sweets and tobacco would be distributed before the inmates filed quietly out of the dining hall to spend the rest of the day 'in a pleasant manner' decreed by the guardians.

· *A Lancashire Christmas* ·

Snow adds a seasonal touch to this Oldham scene outside
the old Town Hall, which now houses the Crown Court

Depending on the generosity of the master, the rules were
relaxed, and mothers received their children and talked with
their husbands for a period during the afternoon.

At tea time the inmates emerged from their day rooms for
bread, margarine and jam, followed by currant cake and the
usual pint pot of tea. Here the feasting ended. They then made
their way back to the day rooms, where the rest of Christmas
Day was spent until the bell rang at eight o'clock for bed and
lights out. In the sparsely-furnished day rooms the windsor
chairs formed a circle around the coal fire burning in the
hearth, with each inmate claiming his personal chair and
position. The floor was bare, apart from a square of coconut
matting in front of the hearth. The only other furniture in the
room was a table which on Christmas Day would hold papers
and books donated by local worthies. A lone gas jet spluttered

in the centre of the room, and helped the firelight to warn off the black, bleak night staring through the curtainless windows.

By eight o'clock Christmas Day was over for the paupers. Boxing Day? That was indistinguishable from any other.

The Workhouse Privileged

Mollie Carney's account of a workhouse Christmas in 1907 does not paint a very enticing picture of institutional life. Yet fifty years earlier, as Raymond Hargreaves recalls in Victorian Years, Bolton 1850–1860, *there was a real feeling among the comfortably-off that those inside were more fortunate than perhaps thousands of work-starved families in the teeming little streets around. That was the background to the great 1857 debate about whether workhouse residents should enjoy their usual Christmas treat, as reported in the* Bolton Chronicle *of 26 December that year. The guardians voted that they should not – but Mr Hargreaves tells us that the following week, the* Chronicle *recorded that the feast went ahead after all, with a local MP footing the bill.*

The Chairman, in moving the resolution of which he gave notice last week, that the inmates of both workhouses be treated to roast beef and plum pudding as usual on Christmas Day, said that he was sorry there was to be so much opposition to it . . .

Mr Cooper, the Assistant Clerk, had prepared a statement of the probable cost, with the proportion each township would have to contribute. From this it would appear that the total cost would be £21 3s. 5d., of which some townships would have to contribute only 11d., and other, who had no inmates in the workhouse, nothing. In the amount stated, credit was not taken for food left, which would be used on the following day, thus reducing the amount by about £2, and if they made allowance also for the saving of the usual dinner, the actual cost would probably be reduced to £17. Mr Latham begged to move that the inmates of both workhouses have their usual Christmas treat.

Mr Alderman Dunderdale seconded the motion.

Mr Nuttall opposed it, and thought that Great Bolton had already enough to do without incurring this extra expenditure. The Vice-Chairman moved that no such dinner or provision take place. He could never support the inmates of the workhouses being thus feasted while people outside were starving. It was really enough to send them to the workhouse.

Mr Taylor said he could not vote for the motion while there was so much distress outside. It was true it might only be a small trifle which some of the townships would have to contribute, but in the aggregate it would amount to a great sum.

Mr Brown supported the motion; it was only once a year they had the opportunity of giving these poor people a treat, and the poorest outside hardly ever passed over a year without a luxury of some sort.

The Vice-Chairman: 'Well, if they have it at their own expense, let them have it.'

Luckier than the starving workers outside? The inmates of
this workhouse certainly seem to have clean and reasonably
bright living conditions

Mr Brown continued that those inside the workhouse had
no luxuries. The Guardians had it in their power to give them
a luxury once a year. Many children in the workhouse were
orphans; it was their misfortune to be there. Many, too, were
widows, and it was their misfortune to be there, and because it
was their misfortune, were they to be deprived of that little
Christmas cheer they had been accustomed to receive? He
hoped not. They could let them have this treat now, according
to law, but not at any other time. Why, then, should they be
so parsimonious as to refuse it, when it would cost so little?

Mr Brearley said he could not vote for the motion. He
thought they should be just before they were generous out of
the public purse. There were hundreds starving outside the
workhouse who would be glad of beef and bread, let alone
plum pudding, and if they did treat them he would rather the

Guardians did it out of their own pocket, and for that purpose he was willing to give £2. He was no advocate for eating and drinking out of the public purse.

Mr Skelton said he should be very glad if the poor people could have a treat, but he was afraid that by giving them one the Guardians committed a very great mistake. He believed that on the day it was proposed to give the workhouse inmates these plum puddings, hundreds, if not thousands, of people in the Union would not have common and ordinary food.

Mr Hopwood said that he must say 'ditto' to almost all Mr Skelton had said. Mr Brown had gone too far when he laid so much stress upon the fatherless and widows.

Mr Brown: 'Fact.'

Mr Hopwood: 'It is a fact, likewise, that three-fourths of the people in the workhouse are rogues and vagabonds, and only one-fourth persons of good character.'

Mr Hodson said that he could not let such an assertion pass unnoticed. The Governor told him that morning that there was not one able-bodied man in either establishment. He sympathised with the poor old creatures, and also with the widows and orphans; and while he studied, as he ever did, the interests of the ratepayers, he would not deprive the poor people of the usual Christmas cheer. He trusted that no member of the Board would lack the spirit of humanity to deny it.

Mr Skelton: 'It is humanity to the payers.'

The Chairman said the bulk of them were old and infirm, and then there were the children. He was an advocate of economy, but would bear his share of the responsibility in allowing the people this treat.

The question was then put, when the amendment was carried by 13 against nine.

Mr Hodson: 'I am sorry for that. The treat will, therefore, not be given.'

Champers in the Trenches, 1915

In December 1915, the winter before the Battles of the Somme, troops of the East Lancashire Regiment were having a wretched time of it in the trenches of northern France, under bombardment from both the enemy and the elements. As the regiment's official First World War history records, however, there was a glimmer of cheer that dreadful Christmas.

As it was impossible to get about without exposing oneself, our casualties were more frequent. Our chaplain, the Revd A. G. Hicks Gower, was wounded in this way, returning from the trenches up the exposed La Brayelle road. A really good communication trench from the front line to Snipers' Square was now imperative. Every available man in the battalion was therefore collected: cooks, signallers, orderlies and even orderly room clerks, and digging for all they were worth got down the required depth in one night. Final touches were added next day to the accompaniment of German whizz-bangs, and the name given to it was Red Rose Lane. This trench eased matters considerably.

About this time our artillery was augmented by a battery of 9.2 howitzers which had taken up a position in front of Souastre, and whose first effort at registering filled us all with

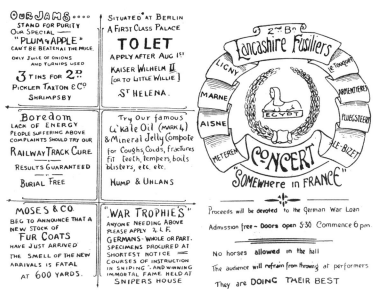

OUR JAMS ○○○○
STAND FOR PURITY
OUR SPECIAL ——
"PLUM & APPLE"
CAN'T BE BEATEN AT THE PRICE.
ONLY JUICE OF ONIONS
AND TURNIPS USED
3 TINS FOR 2D.
PICKLER TAXTON & CO
SHRIMPSBY

SITUATED AT BERLIN
A FIRST CLASS PALACE
TO LET
APPLY AFTER AUG 1ST
KAISER WILHELM II
[OR TO LITTLE WILLIE]
ST HELENA.

2ND Bn
Lancashire Fusiliers
LIGNY   Le TOUQUET
MARNE   ARMENTIERES
AISNE   PLUEGSTEERT
METEREN   ILE-BIZET
EGYPT
CONCERT
"SOMEWHERE IN FRANCE"

Boredom
LACK OF ENERGY
PEOPLE SUFFERING ABOVE
COMPLAINTS SHOULD TRY OUR
RAILWAY TRACK CURE
RESULTS GUARANTEED
BURIAL FREE

Try Our famous
Li'kale Oil (MARK 4)
& Mineral Jelly Compote
for Coughs, Colds, fractures
fit teeth, tempers, boils
blisters, etc. etc.

Hump & Uhlans

Proceeds will be devoted to the German War Loan
Admission free - Doors open 5:30 Commence 6 pm.

MOSES & CO.
BEG TO ANNOUNCE THAT A
NEW STOCK OF
FUR COATS
HAVE JUST ARRIVED
THE SMELL OF THE NEW
ARRIVALS IS FATAL
AT 600 YARDS.

"WAR TROPHIES"
ANYONE NEEDING ABOVE
PLEASE APPLY 2/LF.
GERMANS - WHOLE OR PART.
SPECIMENS PROCURED AT
SHORTEST NOTICE
COURSES OF INSTRUCTION
IN SNIPING - AND WINNING
IMMORTAL FAME. HELD AT
SNIPERS HOUSE

No horses allowed in the hall
The audience will refrain from throwing at performers
They are DOING THEIR BEST

The lads of the Lancashire Fusiliers make the best of it with
a field concert party 'Somewhere in France'. Among items
on the programme were a song called 'The Fighting
Boosiliers' by Private Murphy, Corporal Waddington
singing 'Little Brown Jug' and a Bully Band conducted by
Herr Fray Bentos

alarm. Their first shell fell behind the North Fortin, the next a
hundred yards in front of it, while the third fell somewhere in
the Z.

Luckily, this battery did not fire often. The enemy, on the
other hand, was getting very busy with his artillery. He
plastered the front line with *Minenwerfer* and the village with
5.9 howitzers, causing a lot of damage but on one occasion
quite a lot of good. It was this way.

The gunners had an observation post in the reserve trenches,
situated in the roof of a shattered house which was a favourite
target of the Boche 5.9 howitzers. One day, after a particularly

heavy strafe, some broken glass was observed in a shell hole in the garden, and on further investigation it was found that dozens of bottles of champagne were lying buried there. No doubt the cautious owner of the house had secreted them there before the enemy advance in 1914.

As it was Christmastide this was indeed a fortunate find, and the gunners nobly shared it amongst us all. Christmas Day itself was spent in the trenches, now already covered with snow, but the day passed like any other, except that hampers of good cheer arrived in the line from our opposite numbers, the 10th Royal Fusiliers, who themselves were resting in billets.

With the arrival of the New Year, raids became more frequent on both sides . . .

In the same year the ladies of Bury and Rochdale raised £330 to provide a Christmas pudding for every member of the Lancashire Fusiliers serving with the British and Mediterranean Expeditionary Forces. A consignment for Gallipoli left Bury in November and finally reached its destination in February, 1916, but the Lancashire Fusiliers Annual *for that year gallantly reports that 'the puddings being of excellent quality, they were fully appreciated'. After the Gallipoli puddings had been ordered, however, 'an instruction was received from the War Office that the provision of plum puddings for the Army serving overseas had been placed in the hands of the proprietors of the* Daily News *newspaper, and that this fund would have priority of treatment as to conveyance etc . . . Influenced by the terms and tone of the War Office letter, the committee decided that there was no alternative but to send a sum sufficient to cover all the battalions, and for this purpose a remittance of £100 was made to the* Daily News *fund. To each Lancashire Fusilier who was a prisoner of war in Germany a plum pudding and a box of raisins was sent.'*

The Falklands skirmish of 1981 was famous for newspapers getting in on the act – one recalls The Sun *financing a torpedo on which its reporter is reputed to have chalked an offensive message to General Galtieri – but it seems astonishing to think of circulation battles being fought in the 'War To End All Wars'; rather like learning that Lord Kitchener's moustache was sponsored by Grecian 2000. All in all, the Fusiliers' pudding fund did not enjoy the best of fortunes. At Christmas 1914 only one battalion was serving overseas, and four well-meaning Bury ladies and their friends soon raised the £70 needed to send each man a plum duff and chocolate. It was only afterwards that it was realized that £70 might be seen as a somewhat pathetic sum, and earnest efforts were made to reassure other socially conscious ladies that in future, all their efforts would be appreciated. The great plum pudding debacles serve as a timely reminder that by no means all the battles of the First World War were fought on some foreign field . . .*

Old Sam's Christmas Pudding

MARRIOTT EDGAR

That obdurate Lancashire lad Sam Small was already famous for his refusal to pick up his musket when Stanley Holloway regaled us with his Christmas to-do in 1939. Quite why his exploits were set in the Napoleonic wars has always been a mystery to me, since he comes over as the archetypal First World War Tommy. I need hardly remind readers that the Edgar–Holloway partnership was responsible for a major revival of the comic monologue, most famously through Albert and the Lion.

It was Christmas Day in the trenches
In Spain in Peninsular War,
And Sam Small were cleaning his musket
A thing as he ne'er done before.

They'd had 'em inspected that morning,
And Sam had got into disgrace
For when Sergeant had looked down the barrel
A sparrow flew out in his face.

· A Lancashire Christmas ·

The Sergeant reported the matter
To Lieutenant Bird then and there.
Said Lieutenant 'How very disgusting
The Duke must be told of this 'ere.'

The Duke were upset when he heard,
He said 'I'm astonished, I am.
I must make a most drastic example
There'll be no Christmas pudding for Sam.'

When Sam were informed of his sentence
Surprise rooted him to the spot –
'Twere much worse than he had expected,
He thought as he'd only be shot.

And so he sat cleaning his musket,
And polishing barrel and butt,
Whilst the pudding his mother had sent him
Lay there in the mud at his foot.

Now the centre that Sam's lot were holding
Ran around a place called Badajoz
Where the Spaniards had put up a bastion
And ooh what a bastion it was!

They pounded away all the morning
With canister, grape shot and ball,
But the face of the bastion defied them
They made no impression at all.

They started again after dinner
bombarding as hard as they could;
And the Duke brought his own private cannon
But that weren't a ha'pence o' good.

· A Lancashire Christmas ·

The Duke said 'Sam, put down thy musket
And help me to lay this gun true.'
Sam answered 'You'd best ask your favours
From them as you give pudding to.'

The Duke looked at Sam so reproachful
'And don't take it that way,' said he,
'Us generals have got to be ruthless
It hurts me more than it did thee.'

Sam sniffed at these words kind of sceptic,
Then looked down the Duke's private gun
And said 'We'd best put in two charges
We'll never bust bastion with one.'

He tipped cannon ball out of muzzle,
He took out the wadding and all,
He filled barrel chock full of powder,
Then picked up and replaced the ball.

He took a good aim at the bastion
Then said 'Right-o, Duke, let her fly.'
The cannon nigh jumped off her trunnions
And up went the bastion, sky-high.

The Duke he weren't 'alf elated,
He danced round the trench full of glee
And said 'Sam, for this gallant action
You can hot up your pudding for tea.'

Sam looked round to pick up his pudding,
But it wasn't there, nowhere about.
In the place where he thought he had left it
Lay the cannon ball he'd just tipped out.

Sam saw in a flash what 'ad happened:
By an unprecedented mishap
The pudding his mother had sent him
Had blown Badajoz off the map.

That's why Fusiliers wear to this moment
A badge which they think's a grenade,
But they're wrong — it's a brass reproduction
Of the pudding Sam's mother once made.

Blackburn's Christmas Soccer Riot

When there was a full soccer programme on Christmas Day it always threw up some odd results — often reversed twenty-four hours later, when the clubs played the return fixture. My favourite team, Bury, proved the point as only they know how in 1956, when they beat Bristol Rovers 7–2 at Gigg Lane on the 25th, only to go down 6–1 away on Boxing Day. But all that is as nothing to what happened in Lancashire a hundred years ago, on Christ-

mas Day, 1890. In friendly matches played that day Bolton Wanderers beat Hurlfield 9–2, Newton Heath, now Manchester United, won 8–4 at home to Belfast Distillery and, as is noted elsewhere in this book, Burnley put a dozen past Wrexham. Then there was the remarkable game at Ewood Park, Blackburn, as reported in the Burnley Express and Clitheroe Division Advertiser *of 27 December 1890. That was supposed to be a friendly match too . . .*

Extraordinary Scene at Blackburn

An extraordinary scene was witnessed at Ewood Park, Blackburn, on Christmas Day. The Rovers and Darwen, between whom great rivalry exists, were announced to meet, and 2,000 or 3,000 persons journeyed from Darwen to witness the encounter.

Seeing that the ground was covered with ice, the Rovers deputed their second eleven to face the visitors, whereupon the spectators (the admission being 6d.) demanded that the match should be played as advertised.

The Darwen second team were going on the field, but the spectators rushed at and pushed the players back into the pavilion. Then ensued a scene of the greatest excitement. The crowd's demand for the advertised match to be played not being complied with, they pulled up the goal posts, lowered the flag to half-mast and tore the carpets off the reserved seats in the stand.

One of the windows of the dressing tent was broken, and one of the committee was attacked, while another official had a narrow escape. It was considerably after 5 o'clock before the field was cleared, although it was announced that tickets would be issued for another match.

A similar scene was witnessed at Alexandra Meadows nine years ago, owing to a fight between Suter and Marshall.

> *Those who know their soccer history will not be too surprised at this report, for the 1880s and '90s were notorious for football hooliganism. Indeed, in the context of the 100-plus years of the professional game, those well-ordered crowds of the inter-war period and the 1950s can almost be seen as the exception rather than the rule.*

Festive Burnley, 1890

Even a century ago, a white Christmas prompted Lancashire folk to feelings of nostalgia and memories, real or imagined, of the good old days. 'We don't have the Christmases we used to,' we say today, looking out on green moors and a watery sun. And that, it seems, is exactly how folks had been feeling in the 1880s, and '90s. This is how the *Burnley Express and Clitheroe Division Advertiser* reported the festivities on 27 December 1890:

'Christmas Day opened somewhat dull, with all the signs of an approaching fog, but early in the afternoon snow began to fall, and continued to fall until late at night. This, however, had

All that traffic: Bob Munn's Corner in St James's Street,
Burnley, *c*. 1896

Always one of the grandest of Burnley's Christmas meat
shows: Holdsworth's in Manchester Road

very little effect on the holiday attendances at the football matches at Turf Moor or the numerous church and chapel tea parties in the evening. During the day the bells of the various churches rang out merry peals.

'The thaw of the preceding two or three days deterred some from skating, though many hundreds indulged in this pastime at Lowerhouse and Foulridge, and in many respects Thursday was what many people delight in calling "An old-fashioned Christmas".'

It sounds as if the workhouse tried its hardest for its 420 inmates. Some 150 of them were in the infirmary, but 190 adults and 80 children sat down to 'the usual substantial Christmas dinner' of roast beef and plum pudding in a hall cheered by a tree laden with presents, 'evergreens in abundance and prettily constructed devices'. The *Express* reported that 'At the close of the repast four children recited set speeches of thanks (which had, as usual, been prepared by the master, Mr Adam Haworth) and the motion was agreed to with acclaim'.

The big news in the Burnley area that Christmas included a major fire at Mount Pleasant Mill and a spinners' strike at Padiham, though the workers were back on duty on Boxing Day. No doubt for the families involved in those two stories there was not a lot of extra cash around for feasting and presents, but the town centres of Burnley and Nelson were buzzing with commercial activity, for all that. In St James's Street, Burnley, there were grand Christmas shows of beef and mutton at the butchers' shops of John Hartley, Samuel F. Nowell, A. Holgate and William Collinge, while in Manchester Road the joints hung heavy outside the shops of Edwin Johnson and H. Holdsworth, whose offerings included eight prize heifers from Dumfries and Burnley, twenty prime wethers from Penrith, twenty grand Scotch wethers, two grand calves, six pigs described simply as pigs — Mr Holdsworth obviously did not feel passionately about pork

Trouble in those big snows of 1947 at Lane Bottom, near Burnley.

There was a white-out again shortly after Christmas 1981, but this time people were able to make the best of the conditions

– and one hundred geese and turkeys of splendid quality. But when it came to fowl, a lot of people headed for the poultry market, where Messrs T. and J. Moor boasted a show of the finest Norfolk turkeys, prime fat English geese, ducks and chickens, rabbits, hares and game.

There was no shortage of present ideas, either. At John H. Dickinson's in St James's Street you could buy a nine-carat gold ring for 5s. and a man's gold signet ring with a real stone for 4s. 6d. Altham's Tea Stores, apart from putting on a special Christmas cake offer with every half-pound of tea sold, carried a wide range of fancy goods, toys and novelties, while out in Nelson, Oddie Hartley's Railway Street Bazaar offered – ALL THE RAGE!!! ALL THE RAGE!!! – the New Japanese Decorations, including spiders, flying cupids, skeletons, frogs, lizards, snakes, butterflies, beetles, spiders' webs, locomotives, steamers and engines. Burnley consumers with latent Green tendencies bought their Christmas mincemeat and loaves at Robert Ogden's of Manchester Road, where Health Brown Bread was the speciality. Taylor's of the Market Place made no medicinal claims about their Christmas cakes, game pies, fancy boxes, fondants, chocolates and crystallized fruits; but in Nelson, townsfolk who had failed to stay healthy by eating Ogden's bread could perhaps have found relief in Old Brown's Cough Mixture, available at a discouraging 1s. 1½d. a bottle at W. Preston's chemists's shop in Scotland Road.

The top Christmas shows in Burnley in 1890 were the pantomime at the Gaiety Theatre and Mr D'oyly Carte's Comic Opera Company with *The Gondoliers* and *The Yeomen of the Guard* at the Victoria Opera House. The thought of a band of London-based theatricals spending the run-up to Christmas in the Burnley of 100 years ago is irresistible, but at least they were home by Christmas Day, when Gilbert and Sullivan gave way to a Grand Sacred Concert at the Opera House. This was

Sure to score: stylish 1920s advertising for a celebrated
Burnley product

just one of any number of events held on the 25th. Many of
them had a religious orientation – others, like Burnley's 12–1
demolition of an under-strength Wrexham in a friendly at Turf
Moor, decidedly not; but we can certainly conclude that folks
got out and about on the big day far more than we do today.

The promoters of that panto at the Gaiety took full advan-

tage of the fact that the honest, legal and decent approach to advertising had not yet been invented. 'Altogether the most brilliant and powerful galaxy of talent ever seen in one production' they said modestly of the cast of *Little Red Riding Hood*, which included such top-liners as – dah-dah-dah-daah!! – Miss Vivian Fay Grenville – ex of the Royal Aquarium, mark you – as Boy Blue, the Sisters Millar (the Scottish Nightingales), the Brothers Lisbon (Champion Skaters) and the Lilliputian Rifle Brigade. Even after exhaustive research, I am unable to determine whether the principal boy from the Royal Aquarium was a fish or merely a mermaid. Whatever, one feels that she would have been far better equipped for that other grand Lancashire show venue of old, Saul Street Baths in Preston.

Out at Padiham National Schools there were Roars of Laughter Nightly at Professor Kershaw of Southport's Highly Popular, Pictorial, Musical and Mesmeric Entertainments, and the Queen's Hall in Nelson offered such delights as an afternoon Grand Floriated Carnival and Plantation Ball – no, don't ask – on Christmas Eve, and an evening dance on the 25th.

The Mechanics' Institute was another popular spot. Burnley Vocal Union's *Messiah* was poorly attended, but there was plenty of interest in the Concert Union's Special Saturday Pop on the 20th, when Lester Barrett, the King of Comic Vocalists, topped the bill with such ditties as *You Can't Think of Everything* and *He Couldn't Take Two of Us*. 'Visitors to the Isle of Man will recall with pleasure the *furore* he created during the past season,' blared the promoters, in perhaps a nineteenth-century example of that phenomenon whereby a home-grown singer or group can be treated with the utmost indifference here but is eternally Very Big In Japan. Whatever the demands on Mr Barrett's talents, he was still not too busy to return to the Mechanics' the following Saturday to head a bill of seven in a Great Comic Carnival.

Finally, that 12–1 Burnley win. You'd have thought the crowd of 3,500 to 4,000 would have gone home happy enough with that, but not a bit of it. Most of the Wrexham internationals didn't show, and one of the ones who did was too old to count, grumbled an *Express* correspondent. There speaks the true voice of the Turf Moor faithful, then as now; and, it being Christmas, I bet the pie stall was closed, too.

Christmas was a Little Late . . .

This third extract from Raymond Hargreaves's excellent Victorian Years, Bolton 1850–1860 *serves as a reminder that before Christmas became one of the corner-stones of family life in the years of Victoria and Albert, it tended to be overlooked in many areas in favour of the more pagan joys of New Year. This is what the* Bolton Chronicle *had to say on the subject on 4 January 1851.*

Throughout Christendom Christmas is celebrated immediately it arrives, and the New Year no sooner dawns than it receives its homage. An exception to the rule, however, obtained in Bolton till within the last few years, which still partially remains. Not long ago the natal day of the Redeemer was pretty generally disregarded in this town, and a holiday was

· A Lancashire Christmas ·

Festive spectacular: St George faces the dragon in a medieval
Christmas revival that packed the old Free Trade Hall in
Manchester in 1848

generally observed on New Year's Day. Now, though a
holiday takes place on Christmas Day, the beginning of the
New Year is looked upon as *the* Christmas season, and the
inhabitants betake themselves to their festivities accordingly.
Christmas geese, pies, puddings and beer don't see the light
until New Year's Eve, and Christmas weddings and parties are
deferred till the following day.

This was the order of things in regard to the past festive
season. Christmas Day having passed with its cessation from
labour and its appointed ordinances, New Year's Eve overtook
us on Tuesday, at the close of which day the mills, foundries,
bleaching establishments etc. were closed, some for the day,
others for two, and the work people retired to their homes in
anticipation of an annual treat.

· A Lancashire Christmas ·

The termination at midnight of 1850 was speedily followed by the ringing of bells of the Parish Church and for hours before the break of day sounds of music were plentifully poured forth in the streets by companies of vocalists and instrumentalists, indicative of the compliments of the season. The fall of a considerable quantity of rain seemed not to damp the ardour of persons going about to wish their friends a happy New Year.

The weather at this festive time was quite of an unusual character, frost and snow being out of the question, and the atmosphere exceedingly mild. On New Year's Day from nine o'clock till four, little, if any, rain descended. The town rapidly became a scene of life and bustle, and so it continued until evening approached. Boys and girls, young men and maids, fathers and mothers, thronged the streets in quest of pleasure. The 'festive array' in which many of the Boltonians and their visitors were clad bore ample testimony to the existence of that 'prosperity' which everyone desired to reign throughout the year, and the very 'respectable' nature of the apparel displayed on the backs of the working classes strikingly illustrated the cheapness and plentitude of articles of dress. Candidates for married bliss were moderately prominent in processions, wending their way amidst the 'busy hum of men'. Bands of music passed stylishly through the borough, and added an air of 'harmony' to that of goodwill. The multitudes of country people who flocked to the town in the early part of the day increased the population vastly above its ordinary amount, and the 'fair' was attended most numerously.

The principal streets were crowded to an extent which was rarely, if ever, exceeded. The shops were set out to the best advantage. Stalls with oranges, nuts, gingerbread and other eatable nicnacs, which it would be wearisome to enumerate, were abundant, and there was no lack of toys either in regard to quantity or variety. On the market place holiday amusements in the shape of swinging-boats, whirligigs, etc. were in active operation, and there was an abundance of shows and showmen, professing to enlighten, inform or amuse on subjects natural and unnatural, historical and dramatical, artistical, mystical, gymnastical. On no former occasion in our remembrance has the market place been so densely crowded as it was on Wednesday by pleasure seekers, money seekers and their appliances. Not the least remarkable sight in the town generally was the great number of those who had imbibed to an immoderate extent the infusions of malt and other potent beverages. In the evening, Sunday school and Congregational tea parties were held in different parts of the town, and other means of recreation were resorted to.

The Lytham Windmill Fire

PETER ROSSER

Not many of us think of the Fylde coast as a place of big snows, but when Peter Rosser reminisced on his childhood in 1973 he painted a glorious picture of a Christmas morning horse-drawn sleigh ride through a crisp, white Lytham — until the thaw came. His memory of the

· A Lancashire Christmas ·

The Lytham windmill in its serene seventeenth-century
glory

*windmill fire is an eye-witness account of a famous night
in the town's history – New Year's Eve, 1917.*

This was the year of the sleigh-bells Christmas when it snowed
right up to The Day itself and then turned into a brilliant blue
and white occasion. Father made it memorable by fixing a pair
of shafts to the big sledge and putting in Tommy, wearing
every bell we could find in the harness room and, best of all in
our eyes, a pair of felt snowboots 'like mother's'. We hoped we
were the focal point of all eyes.

For a minute we drew up outside Float's in Henry Street for
the essential quarter of Jap Nuggets, 'one each now, and one
each for the sermon'. Canon O'Reilly's sermons had an almost
standard beginning. 'As I was walking on the Green the other
day, I met a man . . .' from Canon O'Reilly, and a danger-

ously loud groan from father, handing round the Jap Nuggets. 'I don't like Float's,' said Baby one Sunday, taking his. 'They're open on Sundays.'

Then on, on, jingling merrily down Clifton Street through a surely envious throng of churchgoers slipping, crunching and sliding their way on foot to the Half Past Ten at St Peter's.

By noon we were shuffling back down the crowded aisle, the Clifton family, by feudal custom, first – he six feet four inches in his majestic stockings, she six feet in hers, the Clifton children in stockings exhibiting a large 'potato' as they genuflected to the altar. Pace by snail-pace we moved, despite one of Miss Pemberton's extra-tituppy selections from the organ loft. Outside, the sledge and Tommy and the snow were waiting, but the frost had gone. The moment the final rug-parcelled passenger was placed on the sledge, the runners broke through to the roadway. Going home, father leading Tommy, bells jingling merrily, metal-shod runners screaming over the stone setts and the passengers stumping along the slushy pavement, we *knew* we were the focal point of all eyes.

One New Year's Night there was a sudden sibilant bustle in the nursery and we became sleepily aware of a great wind and a red glow that ebbed and flowed across the ceiling. One brother, by virtue of being the eldest, was dressed and warmly wrapped and taken out to see the windmill burning; we others were permitted each a brief turn at the window from which, with flattened noses, we could just glimpse a distant inferno on the Green, red flames and golden sparks pouring into the sky from the mill-top like a giant roman candle. All too soon 'let that suffice' precipitated us back successively to bed.

The great gale, said father next day, was coming out of the north when Mr Shuttleworth had left the mill, after turning the sails back to wind and applying the brake to its furthest notch. But the wind at midnight had backed round to the south-west

and blown harder than ever until the sails – each weighing more than a ton – began to revolve backwards, faster and faster, against the brake; fire followed quickly. Almost everything within the brick mill-tower was made of wood, apart from the granite millstones – even the great groaning gear-trains that drove them. All vanished once and for all – and with them Mr Shuttleworth's 'autograph book', a hundred famous names signed on the panelling just inside the mill door, including, he said '*Sir* 'Arry Lauder and *Sir* Martin 'Arvey'.

Sadly, we could go no more to the windmill with father. Corn, bran and thirds for the horses must come instead from the granary in Pleasant Street. There the milling was done less beautifully, more practically, a stuttering gas engine taking the place of the Great God Boreas. 'Dusty work,' said Mr Shuttleworth, 'but much handier for the Ship.'

Good-bye, Owd Year!

SAMUEL LAYCOCK

One of the giants of Lancashire dialect poetry in Victorian times, Sam Laycock was in fact a Yorkshireman, born in Marsden just over the tops from Oldham. It seems that any

formal schooling received by this son of a hand-loom weaver began and ended when he was six years old, and by nine he was at work in the woollen mills. A couple of years later his family moved to Stalybridge, where cotton was king – at least until the American Civil War of the early 1860s, when the mills were starved of their raw material. By this time Sam was a cloth looker by trade; but he was already a rhymster by inclination, and his Lyrics of the Cotton Famine *struck a responsive chord in countless numbers who heard them. From then on he was an undisputed champion of the little men and women who helped make the millowners rich, even after his verses had earned him a bob or two of his own and he had moved to Blackpool for his health.*

Sam Laycock lived by the sea for the last twenty-five years of his life, up to his death in 1893. He became curator of the town's Whitworth Institute and was a fine photographer, while the sound moral tone of much of his work gave him a firm foothold in respectable society locally. For all this, he never lost that streak of dogged and ironic humour that helped so many of our forefathers keep smiling through their long years in the mill. And in Bowton's Yard *he wrote an anthem to working-class Lancashire life still loved by thousands a hundred years after his death.*

This poem, 'Good-bye, Owd Year!' was written at the end of 1889 and published four years later, the year of his death, in his anthology Warblin's fro' an Owd Songster. *Such was Sam Laycock's mischievous manner that one suspects that at least some of the toffs dining off goose at the Queen's Hotel in the fourth stanza were friendly acquaintances of his from Fylde Coast literary and artistic circles.*

The traditional New Year's Day concert by children of
Whalley Church of England School

Good-bye, Owd Year; tha'rt goin' soon, aw reckon:
Well, one thing's sure, tha's been no friend o' mine;
Soa go thi ways to thoose tha's treated better;
Thoose tha's supplied wi honour, wealth, an' wine.
Aw've watched thi marlocks ever sin' tha coom here,
An', that bein' so, aw couldn't help but see
Tha's had thi friends, an' these tha's nursed and petted,
While tryin' t' throw cowd wayter on to me.

Be off! An leov thi reawm for somb'dy better;
An' tak' thi pampered favourites wi thi to';
Clear eawt ole th' hangers-on theaw has abeawt thee,
An' give us th' chance o' tryin' summat new.
What! Me ungrateful? Here, neaw, just one minute;
Doest meon to tell me 'at aw owe *thee* owt?
Neaw, here's a plain, straight-forrud question for thee:
Come, shew me what tha's oather sent or browt.

Well, let that pass; aw bear no malice, mind thee;

142

· A Lancashire Christmas ·

Tha'rt clearin' eawt, an' one thing's very sure,
'At when we hear th' church bells ring eawt at midneet,
Tha'll tak' thi hook, an' trouble me no moor.
Still, one thing rayther plagues me, neaw aw think on't;
Heaw wilta get fro' Blackpool, 'Eighty-Nine?
We've noa trains leov as late as twelve o'clock; but,
P'raps tha meons to walk, as th' neet's so fine.

At onyrate, sit deawn, an' warm thi shanks weel;
Tha's getten twenty minutes yet to stop.
Sarah, bring up another cob o' coal, lass,
An' bring this pilgrim here a sope o' pop.
Wheer are thi friends to-neet, those pets tha's favoured?
They're dinin' off a goose at th' Queen's Hotel.
There isn't *one* to shake thi hond at partin';
Aw've ole these kindly acts to do misel'.

Neaw, sup that pop, an' eat this bit o' parkin;
Tha's far to goa, an' noan mitch brass to spend.
Shove him a moufin in his pocket, Sarah;
He'll need it ere he gets to th' journey's end.
Aw'm noan a very *bad* sort, after ole, mon;
A chap may love his enemies, tha sees.
Aw think he'll find that moufin rayther dry, lass;
Tha'd better let him have a bit o' cheese.

Neaw wheer does t' find tha's met wi' th' nicest treatment?
At th' sea-side cot? Or 'mongst thi wealthy friends?
Well, never mind; but get thi cooat an' hat on;
Two minutes moor, an then eawr campin' ends!
Neaw what's to do? Come, come, tha'rt cryin', arto?
Aw've touched thi feelin's, have aw? Well, o reet!
Tha met ha feawnd thi *friend* eawt twelve months sooner:
But time's neaw up! Well, 'Eighty-Nine, good-neet!

Acknowledgements

Extract from *A Ragged Schooling* by Robert Roberts (1976) reprinted by permission of Manchester University Press. 'When Santa Claus Forgot' first published in *Lancashire Life*, December 1981, and reprinted by permission of the author. 'Stage Struck' first published in *Lancashire Life*, December 1976, is reprinted with acknowledgements to the copyright holders. 'Sayin' Mi Piece' first published in *Lancashire Life*, December 1975, is published by permission of the author. Extract from *Look Back with Love* by Dodie Smith (Heinemann, 1974) reprinted by permission of Film Rights Ltd. 'Christmas Card Scene', first published in *The Goldfish Speaks from Beyond the Grave* by Jim Burns (Salamander, 1976) reprinted by permission of the author. 'Kisses for the Weavers', first published in *Lancashire Life*, December 1972, is reprinted with acknowledgements to the copyright holders. 'Christmas with Wonnie' published by permission of the author. Extracts from the *Bolton Chronicle* of the 1850s reprinted with acknowledgements to Raymond Hargreaves. Extracts from *In and Out the Windows* and *When I was a Little Girl* reprinted with acknowledgements to the copyright holders. 'The Christmas Bombings', first published in *Lancashire Life*, December 1980, is reprinted with acknowledgements to the copyright holders. 'Flying Feathers' and 'Childhood Christmas of Magic' reprinted from *A Lancashire Hotch Potch* (1989, £3) by permission of the author, from whom copies may be obtained at 46 Penistone Avenue, Rochdale. 'Christmas Blackmail', first published in *Preparing to Leave*, by Phoebe Hesketh (Enitharmon, 1977) is reprinted by permission of the author. 'War Bonds for Christmas', first published in *Lancashire Life*, December 1979, is reprinted with acknowledgements to the copyright holders. Extract from *Mist over Pendle* by Robert Neill (Hutchinson, 1951) reprinted by permission of Random Century Group Ltd. 'The Geese Got Fat' first published in *Lancashire Life*, December 1972, reprinted with acknowledgements to the copyright holders. Extract from *On the Pig's Back* (1987) copyright Bill Naughton 1987, and reprinted by permission of Oxford University Press. Extract from *Spin Off from a Lancashire Loom* (Regency Press, 1981) reprinted with acknowledgements to the copyright holders. 'Owd Abrum', first published in *Lancashire Pastimes* (Burnedge Press) reprinted by permission of the author. 'Quiet in Bethlehem' first published in *Both Blood and Sheen* (Wardleworth's Bookshop, Accrington) and is reprinted with acknowledgements to the copyright holders. 'Tha' wur Theer?' first published in *Lancashire Life*, December 1977 and is reprinted by permission of the author. 'Th' Innkeeper's Wife' first published in *Lancashire Life*, December 1978, and is reprinted by permission of the author. Extract from *Breakfast at Windsor* by Emily Glencross (Richardson, 1983) reprinted by permission of the author. Extract from 'William's Truthful Christmas' by Richmal Crompton, first published in *Still William* (1925), reprinted by permission of Pan/Macmillan Children's Books. 'Christmas Day in the Workhouse', first published in *Lancashire Life*, December 1970, reprinted by permission of the author. *Old Sam's Christmas Pudding* copyright 1949 Francis, Day & Hunter Ltd., London WC2H 0EA, and reprinted by permission of EMI Music Publishing Ltd. and International Music Publications. 'The Lytham Windmill Fire', first published in *Lancashire Life*, December 1973, is reprinted by permission of Mrs Peter Rosser.

All other items by John Hudson using published and unpublished reference material and personal interviews.

Picture Credits

BDCL, pp. 50, 64, 128a, 128b, 130a, 130b; Chetham's Library, Manchester, p. 84; Father Dooley, Judith Shepley, p. 11; DPA and donors, pp. 4, 15, 19, 31, 49, 68, 142; Gloucestershire County Record Office/Gloucester Health Authority, p. 116; *Illustrated London News*, p. 135; *Lancashire Evening Post*, p. 7; MCL, p. 8, 60; Oldham Local Studies Library Collection, p. 110, 113; Peckham's Collection Stroud, p. 87.

(Abbreviations: DPA – Documentary Photography Archive, Manchester; MCL – Manchester City Council Libraries; BDCL – Burnley District Central Library.)